LEAD MINING IN THE PEAK DISTRICT

Compiled by members of the
Peak District Mines Historical Society
and edited by Trevor D. Ford and J. H. Rieuwerts

First Edition Published 1968
Reprinted with revisions 1970
Second Edition Published 1975
Reprinted 1981
THIRD EDITION 1983 (fully revised)

Published by:
**PEAK PARK JOINT PLANNING BOARD:
Peak National Park Office,
Baslow Road, Bakewell,
Derbyshire, DE4 1AE.**

PEAK DISTRICT MINES HISTORICAL SOCIETY:
c/o Peak District Mining Museum,
The Pavilion, Matlock Bath,
Derbyshire.

CONTENTS

Natural chamber discovered in 1779 in High Loft Mine, Matlock Bath. *(Richard H. Bird)*

PREFACE

This booklet has been compiled by members of the Peak District Mines Historical Society in the hope that visitors to the Peak District National Park will not only continue to admire its wonderful scenery, but also begin to take an interest in the many relics of one of Britain's erstwhile foremost industries. Lead mining formed the backbone of the wealth of the Peak District for over 1500 years. The limestone uplands and valleys, and parts of the marginal shale and gritstone country are littered with derelict shafts, grass covered spoil heaps and ruined buildings, forming conspicuous and characteristic features of many parts of the area.

Whilst industrial relics and beautiful scenery are not normally compatible, the old Derbyshire lead miners invariably used local materials for their buildings and shafts, and therefore they blend remarkably well with the surrounding countryside. The 'hillocks', or old spoil heaps of discarded stone and mineral from the workings are now largely grassed over, and could be passed by without a glance if attention were not drawn to them in the first place.

These remains are, however, rapidly disappearing, and the Peak District Mines Historical Society is making efforts in several directions in order to conserve the more important and interesting sites. The excursions in this booklet have been specially planned to illustrate the many facets of this ancient industry, and all contain important sites where preservation is desirable.

We would appeal, therefore, to the general public to assist wherever possible in this task. Please do not damage mining relics in any way, or throw stones into disused shafts, a practice which can dislodge the lining stones and thus render them unsafe. If a site becomes threatened

**A mineral-lined cavity
or vug in a pipe vein,
Magpie Sough.**
(Dr. T. D. Ford)

by destruction, please contact the Society, who in turn may be able to either ensure preservation, or at the least obtain a photographic record and survey before all is lost forever.

Maps

The whole of the area described is shown on the 1:50000 Ordnance Survey Maps Sheets 199 (Buxton, Matlock and Dovedale) and 110 (Kinderscout and Castleton). The White Peak and other 1:25000 maps (2½ inches to 1 mile) will be useful. They are Sheets SK 05, SK 15, SK 16, SK 17, SK 18, SK 25, SK 26, SK 27, SK 35, SK 36.

The Geological Survey 1:50000 maps 99 and 112 and the 1:25000 maps SK 16 (Monyash), SK 17 (Millers Dale), SK 18 (Castleton) and SK 25/26 (Matlock) add detail on the distribution of rock formations and minerals.

National Grid References are given throughout the text for easy location of places mentioned. The figures given in the margins of the sketch-maps are the 1 kilometre squares of the National Grid. All references fall within the 100 km. Square SK.

Rights of Way

Whilst most of the walks described herein are over public roads and footpaths, some of the mining relics are on private land and permission to visit them should be sought at the nearest farm. In any case visitors should observe the Countryside Code of good behaviour. Close gates, take home litter, be careful about fire dangers, and do not interfere with livestock, walls or farming equipment. Other routes described involve the use of cars. Drivers are requested to take care about parking, and not to block gates or narrow lanes.

Safety

On many of the old mining areas there are still open shafts, some unfenced. Take great care when walking through long grass that it does not conceal a shaft. Do not let children or pets play in such areas. Many old shafts are covered with a heap of stones which may collapse with little provocation. Make sure that heaps of stones are safe before climbing on them. Keep children away in any case – a loose stone can so easily cause a sprained ankle. Open mine entrances should only be entered with good reliable lighting. Do not let children go in with only a box of matches – there may be a concealed shaft in the floor! Exploration of old workings is best undertaken in the company of experts. Intending visitors should contact the Peak District Mines Historical Society for advice and assistance.

New Engine Mine, Sir William Hill ➡
(H. M. Parker)

6

TYPICAL SPECIMENS OF PEAK DISTRICT MINERALS

Banded galena and baryte. Dirtlow Rake, Castleton.

Calcite with blobs of sphalerite. Castleton.

Banded fluorspar with galena. Crich.

Galena encrusted with baryte, Dirtlow Rake, Castleton.

Galena cubes on calcite. Matlock.

Cubic crystals of fluorspar, Smalldale, Bradwell.

INTRODUCTION
Part One
LEAD ORE & VEINS

The mineral veins of the Peak District are contained in the Carboniferous Limestone rocks and associated basalt lavas, and it is perhaps useful if these are described briefly first, before going into more detail on the veins and their minerals.

The limestones of the Peak District were formed as sediment on the floor of the sea in the Carboniferous period of

geological time, roughly 330 million years ago. The sea was clear and shallow and was inhabited by innumerable shell-fish, corals, sea-lilies, and microscopic sea-weeds. When these died their remains accumulated as layer upon layer of shell debris which became hardened with time into limestone. It is these layers which now outcrop as the strata of the dale sides, and

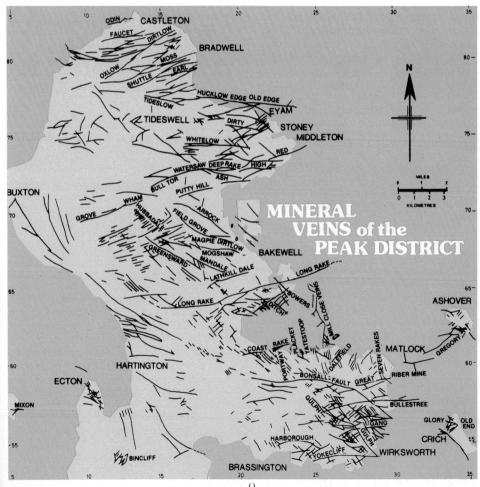

MINERAL VEINS of the PEAK DISTRICT

9

The Lead Ores and Veins

which were penetrated by the old miner in his search for lead ores. Around the fringes of the limestone area there was a series of reefs of coral and other limestone, so that in some ways the Derbyshire limestone area may be likened to a Pacific atoll today. These reefs of poorly stratified limestone outcrop at Castleton and in Dovedale. The reefs and shallow seas of Carboniferous times had a scatter of small spluttering volcanoes, which poured out lava and ashes onto the sea floor from time to time. These are now seen as occasional dark bands along the dale sides, as for instance, near Ashford-in-the-Water, and Chee Dale. The miner had a variety of names for the lavas and ashes, such as "channel" and "cat-dirt", but all are collectively known as "toadstones". This name may be derived from "todt stein", the German for dead or unproductive stone, since the lead veins are usually poor in minerals; or it may refer to its toad-like colouring of mottled green and brown, or it may be an expression of disgust when the miner encountered it .... "t'owd .... stone again"!

The study of the relation of the limestones, toadstones, and veins provided an important part of the foundations of the science of geology in the late 18th century and early years of the 19th century, and names such as John Whitehurst, White Watson, John Farey, Elias Hall, and William Martin became internationally known through their inspired writings on the Derbyshire mines, strata and fossils. The lead ore of the Peak District is the common mineral galena, lead sulphide, and it is found in association with a variety of other minerals in veins of various types within the limestone and toadstones. To understand the nature of the mines and the reasons why certain mining practices were carried out, it is necessary to appreciate both the varied character of the

veins, and the associations of minerals within them, and these may be classified into four types:

Rakes are the major veins running across country for a mile or more, consisting of minerals filling a fracture or fissure in the limestone which is usually nearly vertical.

The fissure may be anything up to 20 feet in width, occasionally more, and many of them have been mined to depths of over 500 feet. None has ever been followed downwards until it closed up, as water difficulties interfered with deep mining. A rake thus consists of a nearly vertical wall with minerals up to 20 feet wide, 500 feet or more deep, and often a mile or more in length, with a few extending four or five miles. The obvious choice of mining methods has been by shafts sunk at intervals along the length, with accompanying hillocks of waste now demonstrating their position. From the shafts underground levels lead into stopes, cavities from which the mineral fill has been removed.

Scrins are minor equivalents of rakes. They are veins usually not more than a foot in width, and rarely coursing across country for more than a quarter of a mile or so. Workings do not often penetrate to depths greater than 200 feet. As with rakes, scrins are marked on the surface by lines of waste hillocks, and often with smaller shafts set close together. Scrins are often found in swarms which may branch out of rakes. A gradation in size between rakes and scrins means that the two terms are somewhat interchangeable when applied to veins of intermediate size.

Flats are mineral deposits lying more or less parallel to the stratification of the enclosing limestone, which is usually not far removed from the horizontal in Derbyshire. Examples are in the Golconda

The Lead Ores and Veins

Mine at Brassington, on Masson Hill, and on Bonsall Moor. They are often very irregular in shape. As their outcrop may have been very limited, discovery was by following a rake or scrin downwards by shafts. Levels were then driven out along the flats. Surface traces of old workings in flats look like an irregular variation of workings on a swarm of scrins.

Pipes are irregular associations of cavity-fillings, replacements of limestone by ore-minerals and masses of alluvial mineral concentration in ancient caves. Pipes are not uncommon, spreading out along the stratification of the enclosing limestone alongside rakes, so that only underground exploration of old shafts can reveal their presence. This feature is also apparent in old documents where a single vein may be referred to as either a rake or a pipe, e.g. Mandale Mine was in a rake with pipe-like extensions in the walls, and the vein is variously recorded as Mandale Rake and Mandale Pipe.

All four of these types of vein are found enclosed in the Carboniferous limestone of the Peak District, which may be studied in the cliffs along many of the dales. These cliffs show to advantage many examples where the veins cut through the limestones, e.g. Lathkill Dale.

The minerals of the vein were formed by crystallisation from solutions of hot fluids emanating from within the earth long after the formation of the limestones and toadstones. Both events may be dated by radio-active isotope methods. The age of the limestones and the toadstones is about 330 million years, whilst the minerals were emplaced in episodes between 270 and 180 million years ago.

The mineralising fluids flowed through the limestones cooling as they went, and deposited the minerals on the walls of the fractures, or in ancient cave-systems, to form the veins. The toadstones,

being relatively impervious, formed local barriers to flow, and thus often controlled the disposition of veins. Rakes and scrins often closed up and lost their mineral content in toadstones though they might reappear in the limestones beneath, as in Seven Rakes Mine at Matlock, and in Millclose Mine. Flats and pipes often either lie on toadstone, or are roofed by a toadstone according to the prevalent direction of flow. Part of the limestone area was converted to the mineral dolomite, locally known as dunstone, which is much more porous, and some flats and pipes occur at the junction of dolomite with the relatively impervious limestone, e.g. Portaway Mine at Winster, Golconda Mine at Brassington and several on Masson Hill.

The lead mineral sought by the miners was galena, which is easily recognisable by its silvery metallic lustre on a freshly broken surface. Few veins contained more than 10% of galena (which contains 86% lead metal) and then not consistently over a distance. An average yield was probably about 5%, though veins with as little as 2% seem to have been worked, probably at a loss, in the hope of the lead content improving further on. Associated with galena there is sphalerite, also known as blende or black jack, actually zinc sulphide. This usually occurs in much smaller proportions, and if worked at all was generally only a by-product used as a source of zinc in brass making.

In a few areas the lead and zinc sulphides have been oxidised to the carbonates, cerussite (lead carbonate) and smithsonite (zinc carbonate – commonly known as calamine). The former has been worked as white lead ore, used in paint, and the veins containing it were often known as white rakes, e.g. at Brassington, Hucklow Edge and at Wardlow. The latter has been worked also for paint

The Lead Ores and Veins

manufacture, more commonly for brass making and for medical purposes.

Production statistics are very incompletely recorded but a fair estimate is that between 3 and 6 million tons of lead ores have been recovered since mining began. Zinc ore production is much less and somewhere between ¼ and ½ million tons would be a fair estimate.

Whilst the lead and zinc minerals have long been regarded as the ores, they are found with the associated gangue minerals, fluorspar, barytes and calcite. Forming more than 90% of most vein contents, these were regarded as waste, except for minor quantities of barytes used for paint manufacture, until late in the 19th century. If possible, these waste minerals were separated from the ore underground and was stacked in old workings as 'deads'. Nowadays the gangue minerals are the important product and the metal ores are simply by-products.

Fluorspar, calcium fluoride, is the chief source of fluorine compounds in the chemical industry, of fluorine anaesthetics in medicine, of heat-resistant enamels, and is widely used as a flux in steel processing. Up to 200,000 tons is now produced annually in Derbyshire, and one mining company, Laporte Industries Ltd., operates two large fluorspar mines near Eyam.

Barytes, barium sulphate (strictly now called barite, but commonly known in Derbyshire as 'cawk') is now produced at about 40,000 tons each year. It is used for paint manufacture, for glossy paper, toothpaste, as a source of barium in the chemical industry, and in large quantities in oil or gas well drilling in the North Sea, for example.

Two mines have been worked until recently in a vein which is almost entirely calcite at Long Rake, near Youlgreave. The main demand for calcite (calcium carbonate – the same as limestone) depends on its consistent white colour and it is used in terrazzo floor and wall surfacing. Other uses are in the mixture for white lines on roads, in stucco wall surfaces and other forms of ornamentation. It also finds uses in the chemical industry.

Fluorspar is largely confined to a strip of the eastern margin of the limestone area about a mile wide, through Castleton, Bradwell, Hucklow, Eyam, Youlgreave, Matlock and Wirksworth. It is generally a translucent white to cream colour, but may also occur in various shades of blue to purple. Freely grown crystals are cubic, but break with an oblique (octahedral) cleavage. Blue and white banded fluorspar occurs in the mines and caverns of Treak Cliff, Castleton, and has been worked as Blue John for ornamental purposes since the mid 18th century. (see Castleton Itinerary).

Barytes is an opaque cream colour, without an obvious crystallised form, although occurring in clusters of small imperfect crystals known as 'cockscomb' habit. Its density distinguishes barytes easily, being half as heavy again as fluorspar, and nearly twice as heavy as an equivalent sized piece of calcite or limestone. It may occasionally occur in large white blade-like crystals or with pink bands.

Calcite is found in many forms and in shades of white from chalky to glassy. Comb-structured calcite is a common form of many rakes, in parallel growths of turbid white to grey calcite. Nail-head spar is formed of stumpy hexagonal prisms, with flat rhombohedral terminations, common in association with Blue John or in hollow fossil shells. It is either clear or slightly creamy and translucent. Dog-tooth spar is by far the commonest freely grown crystal form, and takes the form of sharp hexagonal pyramids, often inter-grown, and sometimes with corroded or bevelled edges.

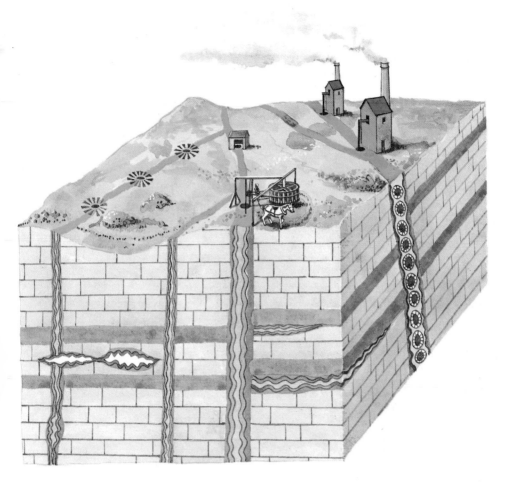

On the surface two parallel rakes are shown with scrins branching out of each. The right-hand rake, worked by two Cornish Engines, has broken (brecciated) ore and gangue minerals. It is in a fault downthrowing the limestones with two included toadstone layers on the left. The left-hand rake has encrusted ore and gangue minerals, and has two flat veins spreading out to the right each capped by toadstones. The left-hand rake has been worked from a coe and from a horse-gin. The scrins to the left are linked by an irregular pipe-vein composed of mineral-lined caverns. There are hillocks and open climbing shafts on the left-hand scrin.

Besides the above nearly one hundred other minerals have been recorded in the Peak District, but most are of academic significance only and are not common enough to be worked economically. Some are so rare that they are known from only a single locality and others were obtained from underground sites no longer accessible.

A full list, with annotations and references was given by T. D. Ford and W. A. S. Sarjeant in the Bulletin of the Peak District Mines Historical Society, Volume 2, No.3, in 1964. Besides these minerals a number of other materials have been mined in the Peak District. Perhaps the best known of these is the Ashford Black Marble, a very dark variety of

The Lead Ores and Veins

limestone, which was mined near Ashford-in-the-Water in the 18th and 19th centuries. It takes a high polish and when inlaid with various coloured stones, including galena, fluorspar, and barytes, was a highly favoured ornamental material for tables, mantle-pieces and other smaller articles. Two other varieties of limestone were also mined near Ashford, for use in inlay work. They were Rosewood Marble, mined in Nettler Dale, north of Sheldon, and Birds Eye Marble, also found in Nettler Dale but quarried at the surface. The former was marked with irregular brownish laminations, which, when polished, looked like the veining in Rosewood; the latter contained white fossil debris, largely of crinoid fragments in a nearly black matrix.

A brick-red iron-stained limestone was used for inlay and small ornamental work, for example the pulpit in Great Longstone Church, under the name of Duke's Red Marble. The Duke of Devonshire caused the whole deposit of this red limestone to be worked out when it was discovered in the walls of a vein in the Alport Mines about 1830, and the exact site is no longer known.

Various yellow, buff, or red clays have been worked chiefly in the Brassington area, as ochre for use in colouring paints, etc.. Manganese dioxide in the form of the black, earthy 'wad' has been obtained from a number of mines, chiefly around Elton and Winster, again largely for use as a pigment.

Copper has been obtained at Ecton in Staffordshire in a very extensive group of mines. The first records of workings were in the mid 17th century but the peak period was the late 18th and 19th century. Judged from the available incomplete records some 4,000 tons of copper metal were obtained, in addition to unrecorded quantities of lead and zinc ores. Working ceased in the 1880's when the price of copper fell too low for economic extraction, but the deposits were never completely worked out. Specimens of chalcopyrite, malachite, and azurite may still be found on the dumps.

Limestone of the Hopton Wood beds is being mined at present in the Middleton limestone mine at Middleton-by-Wirksworth. Some 5,000 tons of this high purity limestone are extracted every week for use in glass making, sugarbeet refining, and the chemical industry.

Winding ore out of the mine by stows (from Agricola 1556)

INTRODUCTION
Part Two
HISTORY

Early History:

Present day historians cannot be sure of the origin of lead mining in the Peak District. Before the Roman occupation of this country, lead ore was obtained in the North Pennines, and so it seems likely, though not proven, that veins in the Peak District would be exploited at the same period.

The Romans definitely worked the ore and several 'pigs' or crude ingots of metallic lead have been unearthed from time to time. The first was found about a foot beneath the surface on Cromford Nether Moor in the year 1777. Since then others have been found at Matlock Bank, Tansley Moor and Bradwell; several others, although found outside the County, some as far away as Sussex, can be traced back to Derbyshire. At least 27 pigs are now known to have been cast in metal obtained from the Peak mines. Most of these have inscriptions on one or more faces and although drastically abbreviated, the owner and place of manufacture can usually be deduced.

The Derbyshire pigs are distinguished by the letters LVT or LVTVD, or in one case LVTVDARES, all of which are believed to refer to Lutudarum. This is popularly supposed to have been located on the site of either Wirksworth or Matlock, but these suppositions are without direct evidence. Chesterfield, as a very ancient and well-established lead market could be suggested or, more likely, the name may refer to the whole area of the mineral field.

A further difficult problem is presented by the letters EX ARG, and despite much speculation a wholly satisfactory translation and expansion does not appear to be available. Several translations seem possible, and include 'ex argento', meaning 'made from silver'; 'ex argenteriis', meaning 'from the silver mines'; or 'ex argentiia officina', meaning 'from the silver refinery'. Two of the pigs have pieces of galena embedded in them and it has been pointed out that galena could not have withstood the process of cupellation (the method of removing silver from lead) and remained unaltered. 'Ex arg' can also be taken to mean 'that from which silver has been removed', but analyses have shown that the silver content of pigs is much the same as in galena. The Derbyshire ores are usually poor in silver content, and with the exception of the Ball Eye Mine near Bonsall (285.574), they would not appear to be rich enough to be classed as silver ores. Dating the pigs is also difficult and only the one from Cromford Moor can be dated accurately to the period AD.117-138.

So far as the actual sites of working are concerned, most of the commercial show caverns at Matlock Bath claim to contain 'Roman Galleries', and some written accounts quote descriptions of supposed Roman workings in Derbyshire mines.

The extraction of the lead ore by the Romans would probably be mainly confined to the open workings along the outcrops of the major veins. Sometimes the veins could be between 40 and 60 feet wide at the surface and, whilst this was not exclusively filled with lead ore, the workings could be taken to a fair depth by opencast methods. Undoubtedly the Romans possessed the knowledge and technical skill required to undertake deep mining, but open-cast working would be a far more economical proposition.

Roman artefacts have been found associated with lead mining operations at Elton, Crich and Longstone Edge. Unfortunately no precise descriptions survive so it is not known if they were found at the surface or underground.

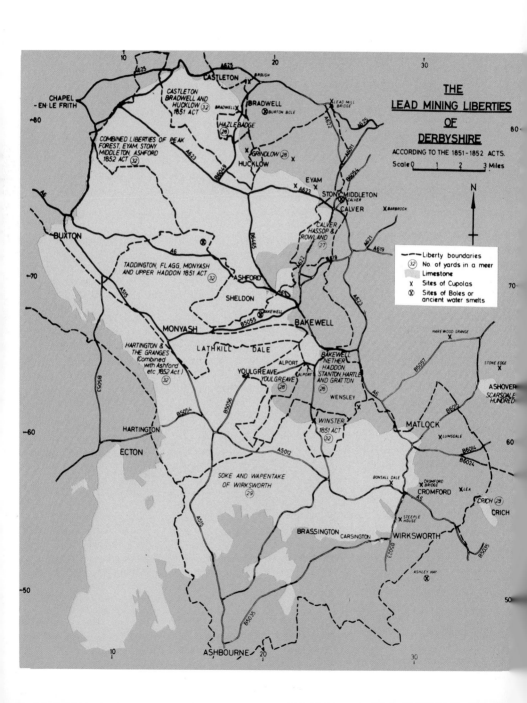

THE
LEAD MINING LIBERTIES
OF
DERBYSHIRE

ACCORDING TO THE 1851-1852 ACTS.

Scale 0   1   2   3 Miles

N

- - - Liberty boundaries
(32) No. of yards in a meer
     Limestone
X   Sites of Cupolas
⊗   Sites of Boles or
     ancient water smelts

CHAPEL-EN-LE FRITH

CASTLETON

CASTLETON BRADWELL AND HUCKLOW 1851 ACT (32)

BRADWELL
BRADWELL X
⊗ BURTON BOLE

BROUGH

X LEAD MILL BRIDGE

HAZLEBADGE (26)

COMBINED LIBERTIES OF PEAK FOREST, EYAM, STONY MIDDLETON, ASHFORD 1852 ACT (32)

X GRINDLOW (26) X

HUCKLOW

EYAM
X EYAM A623
STONY MIDDLETON
CALVER
CALVER

X BARBROOK

CALVER HASSOP & ROWLAND (27)

BUXTON

⊗

TADDINGTON, FLAGG, MONYASH AND UPPER HADDON 1851 ACT (32)

ASHFORD

SHELDON

BAKEWELL
X BAKEWELL

HAREWOOD GRANGE X

STONE EDGE X

ASHOVER
SCARSDALE HUNDRED

MONYASH

LATHKILL DALE

HARTINGTON & THE GRANGES (Combined with Ashford etc. 1852 Act) (32)

YOULGREAVE
YOULGREAVE (26)

ALPORT
ALPORT

BAKEWELL NETHER HADDON, STANTON HARTLE AND GRATTON (26)

WENSLEY

X

HARTINGTON

ECTON

WINSTER 1851 ACT (32)

MATLOCK
X LUMSDALE

B6012

B6014
B6024

A5012

SOKE AND WAPENTAKE OF WIRKSWORTH (29)

BONSALL DALE X

CROMFORD BRIDGE X
CROMFORD
X LEA

X STEEPLE HOUSE

BRASSINGTON   CARSINGTON

WIRKSWORTH

CRICH (29)
CRICH

X ASHLEY HAY
⊗

ASHBOURNE

The History of Mining

The Lead Miners' Dish in Wirksworth Moot Hall. *(Dr. T. D. Ford)*

Recently an opencast lead vein bridged by a Roman wall was discovered at Roystone Grange near Ballidon.

There is a limited number of mines with workings apparently of great antiquity, but, because of lack of any documentary evidence, they cannot be dated. The Nestus (= Rutland) Mine is a good example, as there are workings which had their mineral ores extracted many centuries ago.

After the withdrawal of the Roman forces, there was a lapse of some 600 years before the Norman Conquest. During the intervening period both the Saxons and the Danes filtered into the Peakland Hills and mining continued but it is thought on a smaller scale than previously.

In the 9th century the mines at Wirksworth were attached to the Abbey of Repton, and were evidently of considerable importance because lead worth 300 shillings had to be paid as annual rent charge to Christ Church, Canterbury. The Danish army destroyed Repton Abbey in 874, and the Manor of Wirksworth along with the lead mines passed into the hands of the Danish King Ceolwulf. The mines at this date became the property of the Crown and the mineral duties in the 'Kings Field' still belong to the Duchy of Lancaster. The Kings Field does not cover the entire mining field, and the owners of the different mining liberties will be discussed later.

The Odin Mine (134.834) near Castleton traditionally derives its name from being worked at the time of the Danes, though its name is not recorded until about 1280.

The Domesday Survey, undertaken in 1086, lists 7 lead works. In this context, 'works' means smelting sites, rather than mines, and each smelter would serve a number of mines. One works was at each of Bakewell, Ashford, Crich, Matlock, and 3 were at Wirksworth.

Lead was in demand for roofing and other building purposes, the numerous castles and religious houses constructed during the 11th, 12th and 13th centuries provided a steady outlet for Derbyshire lead.

The metal was also exported; for example approximately 200 tons were

17

The History of Mining

sent to Clairvaux Abbey in France in the late 12th century.

Accounts indicate that mining was widespread and well established throughout the ore field during this period and production reached a high level, though market demand produced wider fluctuations. Thus in the year 1195 the Tideslow Mines had an output of 2,600 loads (about 650 tons of ore) but some 50 years later the whole of the Peak Forest mines, in which the Tideslow Mines were situated, produced fewer than 500 loads.

Origin and Early Developments of Mining Customs:

At this point it may help if the broad outlines of the mining laws are considered.

The orefield is divided into several administrative compartments some of which belong to the Crown, the Duchy of Lancaster; others belong to private individuals. The Duchy owns the Kingsfield or Queensfield consisting of two principal areas, the High Peak and the Low Peak or Soke and Wapentake of Wirksworth. Each area consists of a collection of liberties corresponding with few exceptions to the parish boundaries. In the High Peak therefore Castleton Liberty is synonymous with the parish of Castleton.

Outside the Kings (Queens) field the lead mining royalties are owned by individuals such as the Duke of Devonshire and the Duke of Rutland. Miners in these liberties did not have identical laws and customs with those in the Kingsfield but they are broadly similar.

The lead mining royalties due to the Crown have been frequently leased to individuals since early times on payment of an annual rent. The Duke of Devonshire and Sir Richard Arkwright (of cotton fame) are amongst former lessees of the Kingsfield royalties.

The whole jurisdiction applicable to Derbyshire lead mining, with few exceptions too complicated to deal with here, is dealt with by the Barmote or Barmoot Court consisting of a Steward, Barmaster and a Jury of 12 (formerly 24) miners or maintainers of mines.

Until two Acts of Parliament were passed in 1851 and 1852 these peculiar laws and customs were outside Common Law. The lead mining Acts are still in force and the Barmoot Courts still meet twice a year. It should be noted the Acts do not cover all the private liberties.

Within the Kings field any man could search for lead ore without hindrance from the landowner, only certain places being exempted from this peculiar custom, Church yards, gardens, orchards and highways could not be disturbed in the search for ore, although lead was worked from beneath such places on many occasions.

A vein, when first discovered, had to be "freed", that is, application had to be made to the Barmaster (a Crown official who deals with all lead mining queries and customs), to register the name of the new vein in his book; at the same time, one "freeing dish" of ore being paid to him by the miners. This dish represented the initial payment due to the owner of the mineral duties.

The volume of the Low Peak standard dish is 14 Winchester pints and the original dish presented to the miners by Henry VIII in 1513 is still preserved in the Moot Hall at Wirksworth. It holds about 65lbs of dressed lead ore.

The Barmaster, upon receipt of this freeing dish, allowed the finders of the new vein two "founder meers" of ground. The meer, which is a very ancient unit, is 32 yards in length in the High Peak, irrespective of the width or depth of the

The History of Mining

vein. The length of the meer varies in different parts of the mining area; some localities, for example the Low Peak and Ashford South Side Liberty had 29 yards to the meer, whilst in Youlgreave Liberty it was only 28 yards.

The payment of the freeing dish to the Barmaster enabled the miners to work for a distance of 2 meers in their new vein, and as deep as their resources would allow, the width of the working being governed by the width of the vein itself. The third meer was called the Lord's meer and belonged exclusively to the owner of the mineral duties.

This Lord's meer could either be purchased outright by the miners, or they had a right to work through it, but in this latter case could not sell any ore they obtained in so doing. If they decided to purchase the Lord's meer outright then the Barmaster and the Members of the Barmote Court were called to descend the mine, view the vein, and place a valuation on it. The Barmote Court is still held and although today its function is somewhat traditional, in the mining days there was generally a great deal of work to be transacted and the jury men, who were miners or had connections with the industry, dealt with disputes of ownership, non-payment of debts, and other mining and mineral matters. After the miners had worked, or worked through the Lord's Meer, they could free as many subsequent taker meers as they wished. These had to be kept at work or they could be "nicked" or counter-claimed by other miners wishing to work the vein. Providing that the vein was worked to the satisfaction of the Barmaster it could not be forfeited. Should the vein stand idle through lack of adequate ventilation, or because it was drowned with water, then it could not be "nicked" or forfeited.

In addition to the "freeing dishes" paid by the miners to the owners of the mineral duties, other royalties were also payable. These included both "Lot" and "Cope" and also Tithe. Briefly, the Lot was taken as a certain fraction of the dressed ore. Normally this amount was one thirteenth, but at times this was altered by the Mineral Lords, sometimes on account of the low price of the lead, which made mining less profitable than usual. The Cope was generally paid by the lead merchants and was, in places, 4d. per load, in others 6d. per load. The Cope was taken as payment in lieu of the Crown or his lessee having first right to purchase the ore. Nine dishes were reckoned to equal one load, and the load varied in weight, dependent upon the quality of the ore, so that about 3½ - 4 loads would be equal to one ton.

At an inquisition in 1288 the framework of these curious and ancient laws was set out. They may have been derived in the first place from the Saxons but were not firmly esatblished after the final overthrow of the Danish Kings. After many additions and modications, the Laws were finally passed as two Acts of Parliament, one in 1851 for the High Peak, the other in 1852 for the Soke and Wapentake of Wirksworth the combined liberties of Eyam and Stoney Middleton. Tideswell, Ashford and Hartington and the liberty of Crich.

More detailed accounts of the Laws will be found by consulting the bibliography, but possibly the most entertaining way to read them is to consult the "Rhymed chronicle" of Edward Manlove, first published in 1653. Manlove was Steward of Wirksworth Barmote Court, and he set down in verse the quaint customs with which he would obviously be very familiar.

Early mining by shallow shafts and short galleries as shown in Agricola's "De Re Metallica" 1556.

The History of Mining

Mining Methods: Ore and rock extraction

The process of ore and rock extraction advanced but slowly. Gunpowder was introduced into British mining as a means of rock breakage about 1670 but its use was very slow to spread.

Working a vein outcrop by opencast methods was, as previously noted, probably utilised by the Romans. Indirect evidence suggests that many of the large opencast workings still to be seen throughout the orefield were excavated before 1600. Rich ribs of ore, often found adjacent to one wall of some large veins, may have been extracted by limited underground development before opencasting was undertaken. Examples can be seen at Odin Mine and Dirtlow Rake.

One of the early forms of underground work was by bell-pit shafts. These are usually only about 30 feet to 50 feet in depth with very limited internal development at the foot. Such shafts are generally concentrated in a closely spaced area if on a pipe or flat or occur every 10 or 15 yards strung out like beads if on a vein or scrin. Examples of the former type can be seen south west of Elton village where they occur in great profusion and on Bonsall Lees, west of Slaley, for the latter type.

The earliest precisely dateable underground workings in Derbyshire are situated on the Nestus Pipes-Bacon Rake complex on the Heights of Abraham, Matlock Bath, where exploitation was in progress by 1470. There are however possibilities of earlier underground work at Moss Rake, Bradwell 1242-1247, at Oden Mine about 1260-1280 and at Mandale Mine, Over Haddon, about 1284.

Excavation was accomplished with a variety of tools and methods. Fire-setting was frequently employed: a fire built against the rock face resulted in its being fractured and even shattered by the heat generated. The usage of fire-setting necessitated the introduction of laws into the Barmote Court to prevent fires being lit before 4 p.m. so preventing suffocation of men in adjacent workings.

Fire-set workings can be examined in Coalpit Rake Mine (Devonshire Cavern), Nestus Pipe and Owlet Hole Mine, Matlock Bath. The process was obsolete in Derbyshire by about 1700.

Due to technological difficulties in excavation through solid limestone, most levels constructed before 1700 tended to be driven along veins, joints or similar zones of weakness. About 1655-1660 it was discovered that by driving a level along the sub-surface interface between the shale and underlying limestone, easier digging was accomplished in the shale yet the miners were able to observe any mineralisation in the limestone. The technique was probably first introduced at Bates Sough, Cromford Moor, or possibly at Old Ranter Sough north of Wirksworth.

Toward the end of the 17th Century the Derbyshire miners refined a technique that had been known for centuries. Agricola in 1556 depicted a miner digging a tunnel by means of striking the squared end of a pick with a hammer. Whereas only ore and zones of weakness were previously exploited in this way, by cutting a series of parallel grooves in the rock face and subsequently trimming the sides of the level the expertise was acquired so that it became possible to construct long cross-cut levels in hard, relatively unjointed rock. Progress was painfully slow, averaging about 1½ inches per shift in 1670, reaching only 3 inches per shift almost a century later.

The History of Mining

These levels have become known to modern mine explorers as "coffin levels" due to their often peculiar cross-sectional shape.

Excellent examples of the art can be seen in Winster Sough, Ball Eye Sough, Masson Sough and the Whalfe and Crimbo Mines at Monyash (see Monyash chapter).

Gunpowder blasting was probably introduced into British mining about 1670 at the Ecton Copper mines, Staffordshire. The earliest authenticated use of powder dates from July 1672 when about ½lb was used in Bailliff or Bailey Croft Sough, Wirksworth. After the shot hole had been bored a small quantity of gunpowder, perhaps 2oz to 4oz, was placed into the hole. The use of iron wedges to secure the charge in the hole often resulted in premature firing of the powder and serious injury or even death to the miners. Though a safer procedure using clay or stone chippings to stem the hole had been available in Germany since 1687 the improvement does not seem to have been used in this country until many years afterwards. This factor of danger, together with the expense (powder cost 1/- (5p) to 1s 2d (6p) per lb, equivalent to a man's daily wage), resulted in the continued use of hammer and pick for hard rock excavation until the mid 18th century, though powder was used sparingly at many mines after 1700.

Early drainage techniques:

Two other problems concern the early techniques of lead ore extraction, namely ventilation and drainage. Both were considerable obstacles to the driving of long levels and the sinking of deep workings. By the seventeenth century the workings along the lead veins were generally approaching the water table.

This is usually determined by the contour of the nearest valley floor, but there may be local irregularities due to impervious layers of igneous rock or other geological complications. Above the water table, the miners were tolerably dry, but below this level the miners were quite often in serious difficulties with large volumes of water. Anyone who has explored old lead mines in the limestone in Derbyshire will appreciate that considerable seepage takes place through the upper workings, and although these may be 200ft. – 300ft. or more above the local water table, they can be uncomfortably wet. Before the seventeenth century various types of pumps were in use. One of the earliest methods employed was that of winding water in leather buckets by means of a windlass. Wherever possible water was run off into natural cavities underground, the alternatives being to wind it all the way to the surface, or if a small tunnel conveniently led to a nearby valley this could save some winding distance. Because of the cavernous nature of the limestone, natural cavities or 'self-opens' as the old miners called them, were sometimes utilised for the drainage of the mine-water. Later, many drainage levels were driven to these caves and underground river courses, thus saving the miners the trouble of driving a level all the way to the nearest valley side.

A rag and chain pump consisted of a wooden barrel, internal diameter about 3-4 inches, and about 20ft. in length. An endless chain wound by a hand windlass descended outside the barrel into a water-filled sump and ascended inside the barrel. Attached to the endless chain were either leather discs or blobs of leather. Thus water was lifted from the sump through the barrel and was discharged into either a drainage level or a higher sump.

The History of Mining

Sometimes a series of rag and chain pumps lifted water from a depth of 150ft; each pump about 20-25 feet in length required 24 men to operate it day and night. Only 10-15 gallons of water per minute was raised by each pump so clearly they were very inefficient. The work was physically exhausting for the pumpers.

"Engines" are recorded at several Derbyshire lead mines during the seventeenth century, including Raventor Mine and Bailey Croft Mine at Wirksworth. Ash Croft Mine, Cromford; and Tearsall Mine, Wensley. Contemporary references to them indicate their complex nature, "Ingeneers" being required for their installation and maintenance, but unfortunately nowhere is it stated how they operated. Almost certainly horses or water-wheels supplied the motive power. An "Engine Pitt", 240ft. in depth, was in existence by 1615 at the Dovegang Mine, Cromford; this was possibly a horse-operated rag and chain pump. An underground water wheel installed here in 1651 lifted water from below the sough.

DEVELOPMENT IN DRAINAGE:
Soughs or levels in the 17th century

By the beginning of the 17th century many of the larger lead veins in the Peak District had been worked down to, or were rapidly approaching, the water table. The driving of soughs from a lower contour in an adjacent valley, or from a deeper valley, which could be 2 or 3 miles away from the mines, enabled the water table to be lowered still further. These soughs were to become very much the symbol of the Derbyshire lead miner's skill, perseverance, and endurance. Today some of these soughs, although driven between 250 and 300 years ago, are still in good condition. Modern miners and explorers of

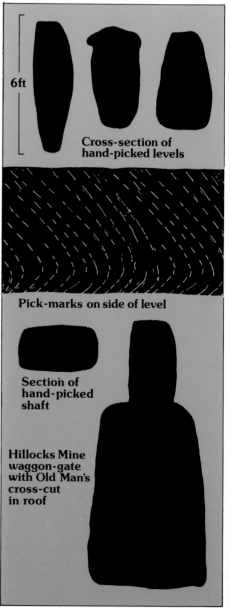

Sections of old "coffin" levels at Hillocks Mine

6ft

Cross-section of hand-picked levels

Pick-marks on side of level

Section of hand-picked shaft

Hillocks Mine waggon-gate with Old Man's cross-cut in roof

The History of Mining

SHAFT CLIMBING (FOOT HOLES)

the old lead mines, both speak in awe at the workmanship in these long levels.

The first sough for which documentary evidence is available is the one commenced early in 1632 by the Dutch drainage expert Sir Cornelius Vermuyden. He had originally come to this country at the invitation of Kings Charles I to direct the drainage of the fenlands and to reclaim land in the Isle of Axholme, in Lincolnshire. Subsequently he became interested in the Dove Gang leadmines between Cromford and Wirksworth. These mines were exceedingly rich but had already been worked down to the water table. The sough was completed as far as the Gang vein by 1651 and the driving of the level enabled the mine to be worked for many years before the deeper Cromford sough was driven. Bates or Longhead Sough (293.564) had been started by 1657 before Cromford Sough was begun, to unwater the Godbehere vein, virtually an eastward extension of the Gang vein beneath Black Rocks.

Cromford Sough was probably started in 1673, and its tail or outlet is still visible behind the houses near Cromford Market place (295.567). Part of it has been explored in modern times. It was driven through limestone and shale to Godbehere vein and the Gang vein, although several other veins had been unwatered before these veins were reached. The sough was extended at various periods and branch levels driven from it; by 1800 it extended in one direction almost beneath Wirksworth.

Other large soughs under construction at this time were the Hannage Sough, commenced about 1693 at Willowbath Mill and driven to the mines north of Wirksworth; the Cockwell Sough at Ashover; the Winster Sough started in 1687 draining the Portaway Pipe and the sough started in 1663 or just before to take water from the old and rich Odin vein, near Castleton.

More than thirty soughs existed by 1700.

25

The History of Mining

Ventilation:

Ventilation was the second major problem confronting the miners, and in conjunction with the water hazard, it persisted until the last part of the 19th century. The working levels became deeper, and the exploratory cross-cuts and the soughs became longer, both needing better and more efficient means of bringing fresh air to the 'forefield' or working face. Some of the soughs were driven through shale, and the deadly firedamp and other gases given off by this formation made the problem more acute.

Initially, fire-setting created a major ventilation problem; the volumes of smoke and fumes produced restricted its use to after 4 p.m. so as not to endanger life. Nevertheless the fumes lingered hours after the overnight fires had been extinguished. Fire-setting as a means of rock breakage became obsolete in Derbyshire about 1700 but ironically the new technology of gunpowder blasting did little to alleviate the situation.

The easiest way of solving the problem was by the provision of closely spaced air shafts. A feature of most early soughs are the numerous air shafts sunk along their course; good examples can be seen at Foolow Edge Sough, an early sough to Bowers Rake near Alport and Oden (Peakshill) Sough.

Bellows blowing fresh air along the metal or wooden pipes were in use from the 17th century. At Cromford Sough, driven in shale deep beneath Cromford Moor, two closely parallel passages were connected at regular intervals and linked to air shafts constructed in order to create circulation of air. Very probably a 'fire house' was erected over the shaft; a bucket of burning coals suspended in this shaft promoting circulation by acting as an upcast shaft. 'Firehouses' on such shafts became a common feature of Derbyshire lead mines and soughs in the 18th century.

SHAFT CLIMBING (LADDERS)

26

SHAFT CLIMBING (WOOD STEMPLES)

The History of Mining

Fans may have been introduced in 1713 at Foolow Edge Sough though in 1724 reference to a 'fan house' at Orchard Mine, Winster suggests something more elaborate. There is a lapse of many years before fans are next recorded at the great Hill Carr Sough in the late 1770's.

Preparation of ore ready for smelting:

Once above ground, the ore had to be dressed before being smelted. The lead ore was known under different names as it passed through the various dressing processes, before being smelted in the furnace. When raised from the mine, the ore was known as 'fell' or 'bouse' and this was initially sorted on the 'bank' or 'striking floor'. Rich pieces, known as 'bing' were taken immediately to the ore house or 'bingstead'. The remainder was dressed, generally by women or boys, using hammers called 'buckers', and was crushed to about the size of peas. This was then sieved in a vat of water. The sieve was immersed in the vat and at the same time agitated. During this operation the lighter rock and gangue minerals are partially separated from the heavier lead ore, and are skimmed off and thrown on the hillock. Large pieces of ore were hand picked and

taken to the ore house. The size of the sieves varied, being sometimes ⅜ inch diameter mesh, and sometimes ¼ inch. This ore was known as 'peasy ore' and the material passing through the sieves, 'smitham' or 'offal'. The final stage of the dressing room was known as 'buddling' and this operation consisted of the remaining ore and sludge being washed over an inclined elongated trough. The material was raked across a stream of water, and the lighter rock and mineral particles remained at the top while the heavier lead fines were deposited at the

27

"Buddling" lead ore as shown by Agricola in 1556

JIGGING MACHINE

BUDDLING

Jigging and buddling ore

The History of Mining

bottom of the buddle by the action of gravity. The smallest kind of lead ore was called 'belland' and some fields near to lead dressing floors and smelting sites are still today known as 'Belland field'. Sometimes old miners, or more particularly women, would rewash the old hillocks for the small quantity of lead left by the former miners.

The introduction of the sieve into Derbyshire is usually attributed to one William Humphray in the year 1565, but at the same time it was counterclaimed that in fact Burchard Kranich had already used the method about 1530 and that upwards of 2,000 poor people had made their livelihood by sieving on the old hillocks. The buddle was also reputedly introduced into the county at about the same period. Previously a good deal of the fine ore had been discarded, having only been dressed by hammers, so this would explain why so many people found it profitable to re-work the old hillocks. Strawberry Rake, lying south of Coombs Dale, and associated with the large vein known as Deep Rake, was the scene of some of these very early 16th century reworkings of old hillocks.

Lead smelting prior to 1700:

The techniques employed in the actual smelting of the lead ore also advanced during this time, again as a result of work done by William Humphray, although Burchard claimed that he had used Humphray's methods some time previously. The ancient manner of smelting had been done by 'Boles', sited on west-facing hilltops to take advantage of the prevailing wind in forcing a draught. These smelting places were extremely crude and consisted merely of a low wall of stones, a few feet in diameter, with an opening facing the wind. A channel led

from the interior of the bole to a small basin into which ran the melted lead. The ore was placed on a layer of wood followed by further layers of wood and ore repeated several times. If the wind was strong enough, at least a partial smelting of the ore resulted, and a pig of lead could be cast. The slags, which contained a recoverable percentage of lead, were re-smelted using charcoal as an additional fuel to the wood in order to obtain the requisite higher temperature. These slags were called 'black slags'. The map of Derbyshire and the adjacent South Yorkshire hills are dotted with 'Bole Hills', each marking the site of a former smelting hearth, although caution must be exercised in the interpretation of the meaning of some of the Sheffield area Bole Hills, as some undoubtedly refer to ironstone smelting sites.

The first major change in smelting methods came in the mid 16th century with the introduction of the true furnace. William Humphray was granted Letters Patent in 1565 for smelting lead ore with a furnace blown by bellows. He subsequently built a smelting mill on the River Sheaf at Beauchief, south of Sheffield, and leased some lead mines near Calver. Humphray claimed that Burchard had infringed his rights, but it is clear that although Burchard had made lead in 1552-53, with a furnace which used a water wheel to work the bellows, it was different in its design from Humphray's furnace. The Burchard furnace was situated at Duffield. A commission established to investigate the claims of both men described Humphray's furnace as having a 'workstone' and the ore being stirred by workmen during the process. In 1581 it was noted that Humphray's was a continuous process. Whilst Burchard probably introduced a water blown

30

The History of Mining

bellows furnace before Humphray, the latter's furnace was obviously quite different, and it is evident that the construction and mode of operation were also different. Nearly one hundred and eighty years were to pass before the introduction of a new type of smelting furnace.

The 'heyday' of lead mining: The years 1700-1750:

The opening of the 18th century proved to be the dawn of a particularly active period, and during the next 190 years saw the industry rise to a peak of technological advance, and a zenith of ore production. It witnessed also the beginning of the decline which was to terminate in the mid 20th century, with the ultimate closing of virtually all mines as purely lead producers, and the parallel growth from about 1900 of the fluorspar industry. The 18th century saw the introduction of the steam engine as a motive power for pumping in the Peak lead mines, the driving of the major soughs, and later, of the first signs of capitalised mining in the district.

A very limited amount of capital had been available in the 17th century and wealthy London merchants and local lead merchants and smelters became partners in mines without apparently encouraging any technological advances. They provided a certain proportion of the finance for the day to day working of the mines, which perhaps may have been difficult for the working miner/shareholder to contribute on his own.

The early years were characterised by the discovery of extensions of several old and well tried veins. The Hucklow Edge Vein had been worked during the 17th century west of the village of Great Hucklow. The mines were initially worked in the upper limestones above the highest lava (Toadstone) and therefore became successively deeper as the vein approached the village of Great Hucklow. Not until the 1760's was an attempt made to sink through this bed of toadstone and work the vein in the limestone beneath. The vein was also very 'shackey' or cavernous and in the latter half of the 17th century drainage levels had been driven and their water turned underground into these 'Shacks' or 'self opens' as the old miners termed them. At Great Hucklow, the vein disappears beneath the overlying Edale Shales, and this covering becomes progressively thicker as the vein ranges eastwards under Eyam Edge, until at the Ladywash mine, north of Eyam village, a total thickness of 796 feet of shales and gritstone had to be sunk through before the underlying limestone was reached.

About 1711, it was realised that this large vein was ranging in a general eastwardly direction, running approximately parallel with the scarp face of Eyam Edge. Almost simultaneously several mines, amongst them, Little Pasture, Haycliffe, and Middleton Engine, all of which had previously worked other veins lying south of the Hucklow Edge vein, began cutting shale-gates northwardly to locate the extension of the main vein, which they presumed would range across the northern end of their ground. These shale-gates not only acted as trial levels, but later when signs of the vein had been seen in the shale, and shafts had been sunk down to the actual vein itself, they acted as drainage levels and were titled soughs on mining plans. They were, in actual fact, not true soughs, but pumpways, not being deep enough to intersect the vein, but at the same time saved 200 or 300 feet of laborious hand pumping all the way to the surface. The

The History of Mining

main engine shafts of the Eyam Edge mines were generally between 400 and 1,000 feet deep.

The vein was extremely rich and ore worth many thousands of pounds was raised annually from its mines. Disputes regarding ownership of parts of the vein between neighbouring mines were fairly common, and one such dispute between the partners of the Little Pasture mine and the Miners Engine mine (205.775) lasted for over 50 years without being successfully resolved. The trouble started in the 1730's and developed because of the discovery of a branch vein, to which each mine claimed title. Adding to the confusion was the fact that it was not altogether clear at the time which of the two veins was the continuation of the Hucklow Edge vein. Due largely to the complex mineral laws, extended litigation followed, which passed from the hands of the Barmaster and the

Pigs of Lead retrieved from the wreck of the Hollandia, which sank off the Scilly Isles in 1743. *(Dr. T. D. Ford)*

Harborough Rocks
Cave
Golconda Mine
Manystones Quarry filled with fluorsparwaste
Dolomite and Limestone
Brick Works
Harborough Rake
High Peak Trail
Nursery Mine
Chance Mine
Old Limestone Quarry
Green Clay Pit
Bees Nest Sand Pit
Old Sand Pits
Condway Mine
Bees Nest Mine
Job Mine
Carsington Pasture
Wester Head Mines
Breck Veins
Old Windmill
Breck Hollow Mine
Footpath
Water Holes
Old Shafts
Old Knoll
Brassington
Nickalum Mine
Sand Pit
Perseverance or White Rake
Flaxpiece
Young Flaxpiece Rake
Children's Fortune
Sheep-folds
Innocent Mine
Kings Chair
Old Harpur
Upper Harpur
Carsington Pasture Cave
New Townhead Mine
Greatrake Mine
Old Townhead Mine
Oakcliffe Rake
Old Lead Mine
Carsington
Reservoir

The Eyam-Stoney Middleton Area

Return to Housley and take the road up to Bretton Edge. Along the foot of the Edge is a line of old hillocks marking the sites of mines on Hucklow Edge Rake west of Ladywash Mine. Lines of small hillocks at right angles to the Rake indicate the positions of early soughs driven to each of the Black Engine, Middleton Engine, Bradshaw, Slaters and Silence Mines. These early soughs were cut through shale and water was then pumped up the shafts and drained out to the lower ground to the south. From the Barrel Inn at Bretton (200.779) a fine view may be had over the whole Eyam-Stoney Middleton area and the courses of the veins stand out as lines across the fields. The Edge Road winds eastwards for about a mile past the private drive up to Ladywash Mine on the left. Ahead lies the New Engine Mine with its boiler and engine house still in good repair (224.774). The shaft was sunk through hundreds of feet of sandstone and shale, and reached its final depth of 1,092 feet about 1860. It is thus the deepest lead mine shaft in Derbyshire. The engine was made by Davy Bros. of Sheffield and installed in 1863. It was last worked in 1884.

On the return towards Eyam, the hillocks of Shaw Engine Mine are visible at the road junction ¼ mile south-west of New Engine (222.771). Below the road at the next bend are the hillocks of Brookhead Mine (221.768), and from them there are good views over Eyam, and the lines of old workings and hillocks stand out across the fields.

3.

THE SHELDON AND ASHFORD AREA

2½ inches: 1 mile, map SK 16; 6 inches: 1 mile, map SK 16 NE. Walking distance 3-4 miles.

The Magpie and nearby mines

The remains of lead mining activity at Magpie Mine are as complete as anything remaining in Derbyshire. This mine, with a long and fascinating history, has much to offer both to the serious student of mining history and also to the casual observer. The mine buildings and other surface relics can all be seen within a small area and examined at leisure. The other mines described in the excursions are generally speaking smaller, but all offer varied examples of the lead mining industry, and some provide excellent geological and mineralogical specimens.

The excursion commences in the village of Sheldon (175.688), a quiet old-world village situated on a limestone plateau, 2 ½ miles west of Bakewell, and 500 feet above the valley of the River Wye. The route, 3 miles long, is easy walking throughout and passes the famous Magpie Mine, Mogshaw Mine, True Blue Mine, Kirk Dale Mine and Fieldgrove Mine. Only two of these mines can be visited by car so that vehicle should be parked in Sheldon village or on the roadside south of the mine at the end of the track.

Leaving Sheldon by one of the four footpaths leading in a southerly direction, the ruined engine-house and chimney stack of Magpie Mine can soon be seen upon the horizon. The best footpaths are

those adjoining the school or on the opposite side of the road to the chapel. All footpaths however converge on Magpie Mine.

The Magpie Mine: (172.682). This contains over twenty shafts and a number of ruined buildings; it is wise therefore to stay on the well-defined paths connecting the various points of interest. The property is now in the tenancy of the Peak District Mines Historical Society who use the main buildings as a Field Centre. Each weekend, and often during midweek periods, members of the Society will be at the Centre and pleased to help visitors.

The history of the Magpie Mine can be followed for over 300 years and a surprising number of remains from each period of working can still be seen.

The earliest record of mining on the site is on Shuttlebank Vein, "freed" in 1682 though it is probable that other veins were worked earlier. In the 1740s Maypitts Mine was producing as much as 100 tons annually. The original Magpie Mine was on the south side of the cottage and ore was produced here by George Heywood from 1740-44. Mining was recommended in 1765 by George Goodwin of Monyash, and an engine shaft was sunk at the western extremity of the site on Shuttlebank Vein close to its intersection with Magpie Vein, but at 360 feet depth water became troublesome.

In 1786 the mine was 'given' by the Barmaster to Joshua White, whose shares then passed to Peter Holmes and partners. They worked the mine from the founder and nearby climbing shaft until 1793 when it closed again. The main relic of this time is the rather unusual climbing shaft with

A typically irregular pipe-vein of calcite with strings of zinc ore, Magpie Mine.
(Paul Deakin)

The Alport-by Youlgreave Mining Field

projecting foot-stones, near the long boiler house, sunk 60 feet on Bole Vein in 1789.

In 1801 Peter Holme and Partners, encouraged perhaps by better prices for ore, re-opened the mine again. In order to establish a sound title, they arranged for an employee, Joseph Gregory, to 'nick' and take possession of the mine after which he 'sold' it back to them for one shilling. At the same time Holme took the title to other veins in the area which were not being worked; this was the first stage in the mine's growth. Work immediately began to re-open the old Shuttlebank Engine Shaft, which was vertical down to 360 feet rather than the inconvenient series of shafts and sumps at the old Magpie. This was then linked at 50 fathoms depth to the old workings, an event duly celebrated in 'ale for the miners', and mining proper commenced, but with little success. Like Goodwin before him, Holme was driven out of the deeper workings 'on account of the water' despite the use of the horse gin and barrels to wind the water to the surface, to run down the 'Magpie Drain' towards the Wye.

The next workings continued from 1804 to late 1806, along the 50 fathom level of Magpie Gate, which was carried north-west for about a hundred yards from near the Engine Shaft. High lead prices made this nearly pay for itself – but a cross-cut to Bole Vein, only 15 feet away, led to disappointment for it was full of 'old man', the debris of earlier miners. Nevertheless working continued, and in about 1808 a further crosscut, again only a few feet, took the miners into what they called North Bole Vein, from which, by using an 'old man's sump' they appear to have found the lead finally in about 1810. It took two years more to develop the mine properly, with another and longer crosscut to form a direct route back to the winding shaft but in 1813, in a few

months, the mine recorded profits of over £360. Profits continued until in 1820 the mine paid out almost £2,000 to its shareholders, then a handsome sum for a relatively small mine.

After 1820, production went into decline and costs rose as workings got deeper, and the water almost unmanageable. In 1823 £80 was spent in two weeks on men handpumping water (at about 2 shillings per man per day) and it is clear a deep trial was being carried out to try the vein at depth. It was successful: the ground was 'laid out' by a surveyor, and sinking of the present Main Shaft (with the headstocks) began simultaneously with rising upwards from the 50 fathom level above a sump down to 80 fathoms; the two drivages met, an excellent piece of early surveying, duly celebrated in ale. By 1824 a late-Newcomen-type engine with a cylinder of 42 inches diameter and 9 feet stroke was installed by the Ashover and Chesterfield engineer Francis Thompson, and workings carried down from 70 fathoms to a total depth of about 100 fathoms in the area immediately below the shaft, with William Wyatt replacing Peter Holme as agent. 1827 saw almost 3,000 loads of lead ore, about 800 tons, produced; this was only exceeded in 1871. By the 1830s however, this bonanza was checked, again by water, and work began to explore the area laterally: the 'double' climbing and winding Crossvein Shaft, sunk in 1833, forms part of this phase. By 1835, however, the mine had closed again, for the shareholders were unwilling to contribute to any more 'calls'.

The years 1824 to 1835 were marred by legal disputes and 'violence on the mine', resulting in the 'murders' of 1833. What profits the mine made were absorbed by lawyers; the wily Brittlebank who successfully represented Magpie was described in one account as 'not the only

The Sheldon and Ashford Area

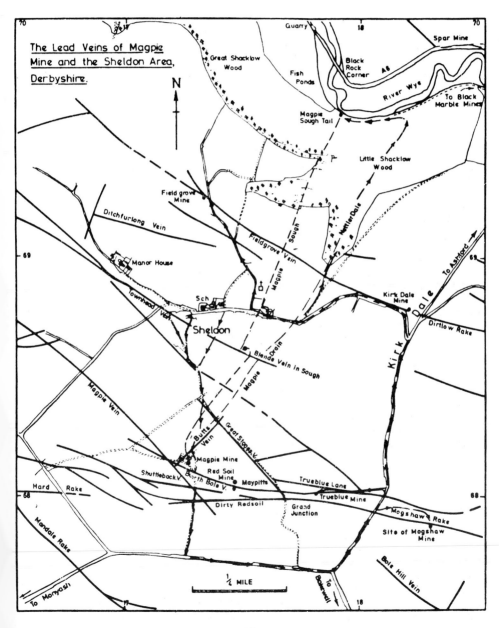

The Lead Veins of Magpie Mine and the Sheldon Area, Derbyshire.

N

Quarry
Spar Mine
Great Shacklow Wood
Black Rock Corner
Fish Ponds
River Wye
To Black Marble Mine
Magpie Sough Tail
Little Shacklow Wood
Field grove Mine
Ditchfurlong Vein
Nettler Dale
Fieldgrove Vein
Sough
Magpie
Manor House
Townhead Vein
Sch
Sheldon
Kirks Dale Mine
To Ashford
Kirk Dale
Dirtlow Rake
Blende Vein in Sough
Drain
Magpie
Magpie Vein
Butts Vein
Great Slopes V.
Magpie Mine
Shuttleback V.
Red Soil Mine
North Bole V.
Maypitts
Trueblue Lane
Hard Rake
Dirty Redsoil
Grand Junction
Trueblue Mine
Mogshaw Rake
Site of Mogshaw Mine
Mandale Rake
Bole Hill Vein
To Monyash
To Bakewell
¼ MILE

The Sheldon and Ashford Area

knave in Derbyshire'. The quarrels began almost as soon as the new engine was put down, when Magpie miners broke through to Maypitt Mine in what both claimed as their own vein. In such a case the title depended on who had freed the vein first: Magpie freed it the day after the breakthrough, but Maypitt had worked the veins since about 1740 or even before, and the local Barmoot Jury ruled the vein was indeed Maypitt. Despite this, in two actions in the Barmoot Court, with a special 'independent' jury, the title of the vein was given to Magpie, mainly on the grounds that written proof of freeing must be given to the Court. It was perhaps a coincidence that the previous Barmaster, who had charge of the records, was a Magpie shareholder, though mining records in general in the eighteenth century were poorly kept.

The Maypitt Miners, who also worked the adjacent Great Redsoil Mine, were thus exceedingly resentful, and it perhaps did not help when Magpie were able, in 1829, to demonstrate conclusively that the vein was not Maypitt's after all and thus lawfully and morally theirs, so that it was doubly unfortunate a short while later when a Magpie-owned cross-vein broke into what was claimed as Great Redsoil Vein, definitely freed long before. It was, however, difficult to demonstrate the vein was 'one and the same' from the surface for either side, and for three years first one side then the other, when they thought advantageous, called in the jury in the hope of a favourable ruling, only to find the other side had placed barriers in their route quite illegally. By 1831 both sides had resorted to violence, with sentries on the surface, and fights underground, and both sides lighting sulphur to drive the other out: the inevitable happened in 1833, with three Great Redsoil miners suffocated, and others injured, by the sulphurous fumes, created by Magpie.

At the trial 24 Magpie miners were arraigned at Derby Assizes in May, 1834. Magpie, again advised by Brittlebank, published a 'Defence of the Magpie Miners' as the accused were not allowed to be witnesses in their own defence, which suggested, with some justification, that the act was one of self defence, and that the Redsoil Agent had sent his men knowingly or with wilful negligence into a mine full of gas. The Magpie miners were acquitted.

Looking back on this it is surprising to realise that the two opposing companies of miners were working within a few yards of each other in what is now a relatively small field. The deaths occurred some 420 feet beneath the newly erected horse-gin on Great Redsoil shaft.

In 1839 the mine was again re-opened, this time with a new group of shareholders, and with the Great Redsoil taken into the Magpie title. The manager was John Taylor, who operated mines in all areas of Britain and as far away as Mexico, under the "Cornish System". No less than 14 Cornishmen came to live in Sheldon, to introduce large scale methods to Derbyshire, together with the Cornish round chimney and round powder house which still survive, and a Cornish 40 inch pumping engine which replaced the earlier Newcomen. The agent's house and smithy also date from this time, as does the strangely out-of-place square chimney: this was then next to a second boiler house, intended eventually for a new engine and shaft which were never built.

Taylor successfully introduced his new regime; he sank the shaft to about 114 fathoms, developed the mine in an economic manner, introduced new improved practices such as cast-steel

The Sheldon and Ashford Area

borers, safety fuse, a steam whimsey for winding and iron-wire rope; he also made drains to conduct surface water. But the enterprise failed when the shaft penetrated a clay bed and the engine was unable to cope with the increased water. His solution of adopting a 70 inch engine, on either a new or the old shaft, was hotly disputed by

Wyatt and his supporters who wanted a sough. Both ideas were outvoted by a third group of shareholders who saw the mine as a perpetual drain on their pockets. Appeals to the Duke of Devonshire for support fell on equally deaf ears for he too had lost much on similar ventures.

Three generations of winding house at Magpie Mine: the Cornish Engine House of c.1869 in the background; the 1913 winding drum in the foreground; and the 1950 corrugated shed. The shaft is beneath the head-frame in the centre. (H. M. Parker)

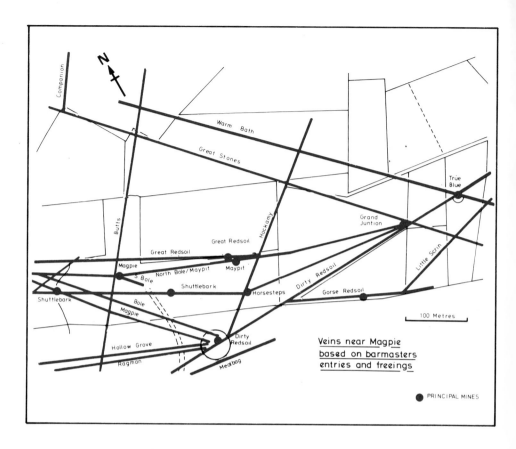

Veins near Magpie
based on barmasters
entries and freeings

100 Metres

● PRINCIPAL MINES

Several attempts were made to revive the mine over the next 25 years with schemes involving both sough and engine being put forward, but in 1864 the remaining shareholders gave up the idea, and the mine, and it was taken over by John Fairburn, a Sheffield businessman, mine-owner and smelter, who created a new company. In 1868 Fairburn moved a 70 inch engine from his Calver Sough Mine which closed in 1863. He erected it in the house which now dominates the site, and pumped the mine dry – reaping the harvest which Taylor had sown. Over 850 tons of ore were raised in 1871.

Prospects at greater depth must have seemed bright, but even this engine was incapable of pumping from over 700 feet depth and in 1873 construction of the Magpie Sough started. It was a financially disastrous, though technically successful venture, draining the mine to about 575 feet below collar, serving as a pump way for water pumped from greater depths. Completion was not until 1881, by which time the engine had been severely damaged in a fire, and the route of the sough proved to be in "Toadstone", hardest and most tenacious of all Derbyshire rocks, for half its distance, stimulating the use of nitroglycerine explosives and pneumatic drills for the first time in Derbyshire but straining the reserves and patience of shareholders, and putting Fairburn deeply in debt. Throughout this period lead prices were falling from the high levels of 1870-71. In 1872 all work at the mine ceased and from 3rd march, 1873 work was concentrated on the sough, probably the last of the major soughs to be built in Derbyshire.

The Sheldon and Ashford Area

In 1874 a water wheel was fixed near the mouth of the sough to power an air compressor to operate a rock drill and to ventilate the sough while it was being driven.

A contract for drilling was made with Richard Schram but after four months trial his compressed air machines and system of working were a failure. The contract was ended and the Company bought the three machines for £250 and worked them in the level using their own men, a method which proved quite satisfactory. The Schram drill was a percussive drill normally driven by compressed air.

By 1879 the sough had reached to beneath Sheldon village, near the point where this excursion commenced. In this year the soughers met an immense quantity of water in powerful springs, and they considered that there was a definite connection with the water in the mine, particularly by draining water from just below the 80 fathom level. It is stated that these springs were met at the crossing of the Townend Vein below the incomplete Sheldon Shaft. This shaft was intended for air and haulage but was abandoned far above sough level after being sunk, firstly through limestone and then about 138 ft. in toadstone.

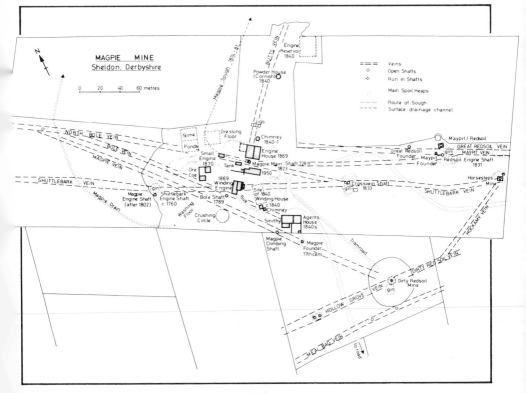

Agents house and smithy c.1840. *(Middletons)*

The sough continued following closely the route of the footpath from Sheldon village and occasionally cutting through mineral veins. Amongst these was the Blende Vein where ancient caves were lined with crystals of calcite and sphalerite. As the sough approached the shaft there appears to have been considerable excitement and indeed not a little danger for the mine itself was now, of course, filled with water. A local newspaper reported 'The tapping of water into the level has been attended with considerable danger, for although the level has from time to time let some of the water down in the mine, yet there was at the time it was cut 108 ft. head of water above them and this would give a pressure of over 55lbs. to the square inch. As a precaution a long hole was kept in advance of the forefield but if by any chance the shots had penetrated to the water and made a hole one foot square, some of the men would probably have been drowned, for although a hole no longer than a man's hand was made first, it had the effect of driving the men forward before the water with great force, putting out their lights and causing them to have to grope their way out in the dark as fast as they possibly could, the water following them at considerable speed'.

74

THE MAGPIE ENGINE HOUSE

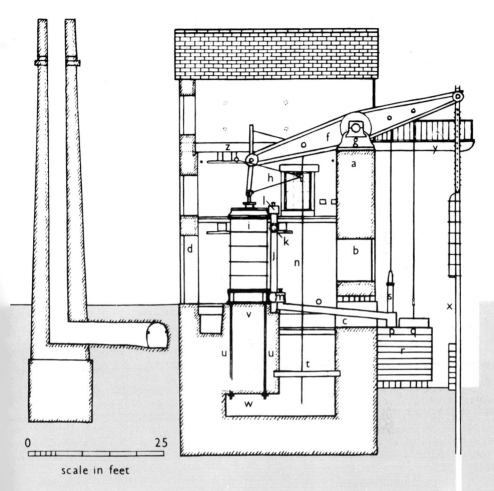

0   25

scale in feet

KEY

(a) bob wall

(b) plug rod door

(c) aperture to hot well

(d) cylinder door

(e) boiler house door

(f) bob or beam

(g) stirrups

(h) Watts' parallelogram linkage

(i) cylinder

(j) equilibrium pipe

(k) live steam pipe

(l) steam, equilibrium and governor valves

(m) exhaust valve

(n) plug rod

(o) eduction pipe

(p) condenser

(q) air pump to exhaust condenser

(r) hot well or cistern

(s) feed-water pump

(t) cataract pit or cockpit containing cataracts for governing speed of engine

(u) engine mounting bolts

(v) engine beds

(w) crow holes

(x) pump rod in shaft

(y) bob plank

(z) spring beams (and side beams)

The Sheldon and Ashford Area

This event occurred on 18th August, 1881, over eight years after the sough had been commenced and according to the Mining Journal 19th September, 1881, "the event was duly celebrated by a dinner to the workmen on Saturday last". The 'Journal' later states "An outlay of something like £18,000 to clear the water and prevent its further accumulation was certainly a bold venture". Whilst the correspondent gave £18,000 as the cost, the original labour cost was £8,000 and other sources give the actual cost at figures varying from £14,000 to £35,000.

If time permits, a visit can be made to the sough tail (179.696) at the end of this excursion. It may be reached either by a footpath down Nettler Dale, or by turning left (west) along the river bank from the bridge at the foot of Kirk Dale, near Ashford, and following the south bank of the River Wye upstream a distance of half a mile on foot. The sough itself became blocked when an air and winding shaft near the tail partially collapsed into the sough, about 1962. Water accumulated in the mine behind the run-in and after heavy rain, early in April, 1966, water was seen gushing out from several places in the hillside above the sough tail, indicative of the great hydrostatic pressure being produced. On Saturday, 23rd April, 1966 the water burst out of the run-in shaft, blowing a crater some 30 ft. deep and leaving only the bottom 30 ft. or so of shaft which was in toadstone. Several hundred tons of shale and scree were moved, a footpath was swept away and the River Wye partially blocked. The blockage was removed by excavator and the sough re-opened by the Peak District Mines Historical Society in 1974.

While the mine was being prepared for re-opening in 1881 the engine house was destroyed by fire, but by 1882 the main shaft was deepened from 684 ft. to 728 ft.; an operation which could only have been accomplished with a pumping engine raising water to the sough level at 579 ft. But despite impressive reports, including one 'of a seam of blende 5 ft. wide', mining operations ceased in 1883 and a trustee was soon appointed to liquidate the mine. In October, 1883, it was stated " the removal of the engine will, it is believed, entail an expense of not less than £150" and in November, 1883 "The immense pumping engine and fittings which weigh about 300 tons have during the present week been removed from the Magpie Mine at Sheldon to the Manvers Colliery, Stanton Gate. One of the beams in the pumping apparatus was so weighty that it dislodged the crane at Bakewell Station, and some of the fittings are so lengthy that they reached over four railway timber trucks".

Except for the small buildings of corrugated sheet steel, the layout of the mine then was much as it is today. The building adjoining the blacksmith's shop had been converted into a dwelling house, and the small lean-to building near the gate was the weigh-house. The round chimney and the round powder magazine date from about 1840 while the orehouse was built about 1869. Together they are typical of any large metal mine of this date in Britain.

The Cornish engine house remains together with the miners' 'dry' (a warm room for changing) on one side and the boiler house, now completely obliterated, on the other. Ore-washing facilities throughout this period remain something of a mystery; the irregular depression near the long engine house was probably a crushing circle used in the 1820s and 1830s. In the 1840s a new floor was built with ore-hoppers and washing grates served by an iron tramway and a hand

76

The Sheldon and Ashford Area

crushing machine, sieves and buddles by the orehouse. In this area there is still a hillock where traces of a building and slime ponds can be discerned. Water from the pump was sent down the fields on wooden launders to the Magpie drain.

For the 20 years prior to 1906 all the operations at Magpie were on a small scale employing only half-a-dozen men. As there was no pump the mine would be flooded to sough level but above this level it would be fairly dry and comfortable. The winding engine remained but it is also possible that the ore was floated out in a boat through the sough. This boat is said to have been 23-24 ft. in length, 4 ft. wide, with a capacity of 45-50 cwts. of ore and to have cost £24 to make.

In 1907 the Magpie Mining Company was reformed by E. Garlick and started work in a larger way but still never employing more than twelve men, of whom no more than ten were below ground. In the first five years the mine produced over 5 tons of lead ore yearly and in 1909 and 1910 some zinc also, but at this time the number of men employed was falling rapidly. About 1913 a new company was formed by E. Garlick, combining the interests of both Magpie and True Blue Mines. Work started with seven men, six below ground, and one on surface.

The winder was "Wingy" or "Oud one-arm" Brocklehurst. Captain Moody was the underground manager and Benjamin Handley his mate. A large Lancashire boiler was put in on the surface for the winding engine and another underground for the Tangye (pulsometer) pumps. Two large pipes were fixed up the shaft, one to raise pumped water for the surface boiler and the other for steam. Also a large 'tub' or tank was hitched on to the bottom of the cage to draw water up the shaft for the dressing floors. The cage was also used for winding men and ore but often the men climbed the ladder shafts. Holes were drilled with a hand-drill. On the surface the ore had very little treatment; it was washed, passed through a jaw crusher and then through a couple of hand jigs or hotches. The quantity of water flowing through the sough at the time is said to have been about 8,000 gallons per minute. In 1919 the mine closed once more, the closure being caused partly by shortage of coal during the strike of coal miners in the neighbouring coalfields.

In 1923 Garlick re-opened Magpie employing a total of five men. However, one year later, the company went into voluntary liquidation.

Very little remains of this period mainly because it was a period of make-do-and-mend.

In 1951 Waihi Investment and Development Ltd., a London concern, commenced to drain the mine below sough level using electric submersible pumps. An electric winder was put into position on the opposite side of the shaft to the old Cornish engine house and a new collar was formed using debris from the mine. The wooden headgear was replaced by a steel headgear and the steam whimsey sold for scrap. Corrugated sheeting was used for the engine house and jig-house, making a strong contrast when seen alongside the earlier stone buildings.

By 1953 the workings had been pumped dry to 620 ft. although in reality water dripped from every crack in the limestone and brownish mud was everywhere. Chatsworth Cavern and Devil's Hole, two large partly natural caverns near the shaft, became accessible but proved disappointing. By 1958 the battle with the water had been lost and with falling lead prices the attempt to

The Sheldon and Ashford Area

reopen the mine was abandoned. Much of the equipment belonging to this period remains in situ and can still be seen.

Derbyshire Stone Limited, later merged with Tarmac Ltd., took over the Title of the mine in 1961 but as yet (1982) no further mining has been undertaken. In 1962 the Peak District Mines Historical Society took over the tenancy of the Mine cottage as a field centre, and a base for their study of mining antiquities. On 24th April 1967 a fire occurred at the cottage which completely gutted the building.

Magpie Mine is a living museum, a place which promised rich rewards but where each attempt to exploit it was thwarted by unseen difficulties with each attempt leaving some evidence of its age. The Magpie Mine buildings are now scheduled as an Ancient Monument and preservation work has gained a Civic Trust Award.

Magpie Mine has such a fascinating history that it tends to make one ignore the other mines in the area but each of these has at one time or another been affected by the developments at their more famous neighbour.

Leaving the mine by the main gate and following the private road southwards, further evidence of mining is very apparent. After about 100 yards Dirty Redsoil Vein can be seen clearly with its line of subsided ground and frequent open shafts, the largest of which is to be found in the small copse to the east of the track. In this copse there is also the remains of a large gin circle and a raised tramway leads in the direction of Magpie Mine.

The private road leads on to the Ashford-Monyash road and this should be followed in an easterly direction for a quarter of a mile. At the first road junction, the left hand road leads down to Kirk Dale towards Ashford. After 200 yards the

remains of Mogshaw Mine can be seen to the right.

Mogshaw Mine: (183.679) is on Mogshaw Rake, which, in turn, appears to be a continuation of the Shuttlebank Vein. The mine is very old and has been known as Mockshaw Mine and Haredale Mine, in addition to the more recent 'Mogshaw' Mine.

In 1768 the 'Partners of Haredale Mine' were given 54 meers on "Mogshaw Old Rake", and also 23 meers in Haredale Vein ranging south-east from their 'New Engine Shaft'. This 'engine' is likely to have been a horse-gin since such a gin is shown on an engine shaft 97 yards deep on a mine section dated 1840. Farey in 1811 recorded 'Mockshaw or Haredale Mine, North-west of Bakewell, shale-limestone and first limestone, lead, toadstone, claywayboards'. The latter comments meant that toadstone was present in the workings and that clay intersected the lead vein. The vein was drained in the mid 19th century by a level opening into a swallow hole underground. The mine was worked intermittently throughout the 19th century at one time in the 1840s by George Stephenson of railway fame. It was never an easy mine to work, partly because of the clay already mentioned. As late as 1889 a miner was killed in a roof fall when trying to drive a level through 'old man's' workings at the mine. In later years the mine was owned by Joseph Smith of Youlgreave producing mainly barytes with some lead ore and 'offal' and in the late 1890s it was worked by G. Thompson of Bakewell. The mine was re-opened by the Middleton Mining Company in the immediate post-war years for barytes. Only a little work was done below ground, the bulk of the mineral being obtained from the surface tips. Little remains however of the earlier working as the mined area has

The Sheldon and Ashford Area

suffered the ravages of extensive open cast workings in recent years.

Two hundred yards further down the Kirkdale road, on the left-hand side the entrance to a narrow high walled grassy lane can be seen. This is True Blue Lane and, if followed, it leads to the old True Blue Mine.

True Blue Mine: (178.680). This

mine is not so deep as Magpie. The foot of the 300 ft. shaft is in toadstone, but workings from the nearby Magpie Mine have penetrated this toadstone and an attempt was once made to drive a raise (an upward shaft) from the deeper Magpie workings below True Blue Mine to the foot of this shaft. It was worked by Benjamin Brushfield in the 1820s and up to about 1841: he spent over £1,000 to deepen it in an effort to reach the same depths as Magpie Mine, failed and it was sold to Magpie in 1842 for £200.

The mine was worked in the latter half of the 19th century by George Goodwin of Monyash and many of the buildings, the remains of which can still be seen, date from this period. The mine was taken over in 1913 by E. Garlick, and worked, with Magpie Mine, as the Magpie and True Blue United Mining Co. The mine was however, never very productive. Returning down the lane to Kirk Dale Road, follow it downhill until the left fork to Sheldon is reached. At the top of the first short hill on the Sheldon road is Kirk Dale Mine.

Kirk Dale Mine: (182.688). There

is no mention of this mine in Farey's list of 1811 but the vein was certainly being worked in 1820 and, by 1841, the mine was owned by William Wyatt, the local mine agent, as part of the Fieldgrove Title. The extensive spoil heaps indicate that the mine was worked for some years, but it had certainly been abandoned before 1870. The mine has recently been worked opencast for fluorspar. From Kirk Dale Mine the road may be followed back to Sheldon village. Fieldgrove Mine is reached by taking the first right hand turn in the village past Sheldon Church.

Fieldgrove Mine: (173.693) is

situated on a vein running from Kirk Dale to Deep Dale. The mine has variously been called Field Grove, Field Groove, Field Rake and Sheldon Field.

Farey in 1811 recorded 'Field Rake Mine, Sheldon, first limestone, lead, very wide in spar', and obviously considered it a very profitable working. In 1828 the mine was dispossessed for 'want of workmanship" and given to Richard Holme. Holme sold it to William Wyatt in 1840 who worked this mine together with most of the other mines already described. Shortly after Wyatt took over the mine he sank the main engine shaft. It is obvious that from the start he also had in mind driving a drainage sough from the River Wye. This sough was also intended to go to Magpie and Hardrake Mines. By 1846 the shaft was 462 ft. deep and the workings were much troubled with water and in 1846 the workings were nearly 500 ft. deep, the water problem being very acute. Despite the water difficulties however, lead ore worth £1,703 was raised between 1840 and 1857 but at a cost of £5,214.

79

An explorer descending Field Grove engine shaft, Sheldon, by wire-ladder. The section cut off by timbers was originally the ladder-way. *(H. M. Parker)*

After Wyatt's death in 1858 the mine appears to have been managed by Herbert Milnes of Matlock and it continued to be worked at least until 1860. However, by the time the Magpie Sough was being driven in the 1870s, which could have considerably relieved Fieldgrove's water problem, the mine had been abandoned.

The shaft furthest from Sheldon has, nearby, a climbing shaft, a gin circle and a tall windowless building.

Nearer Sheldon there is a large shaft now covered by a mound of limestone blocks and nearby are the remains of a further gin circle and more mine buildings. This shaft is the one sunk by Wyatt in the early 1840's. The gin circle is 42 ft. in diameter and has a centre stone with a 4½ inch square hole, which must have served as a pivot. A horse gin, probably this one, was bought in 1841 for £51, together with some metal air pipes costing £28. Following this visit the return journey must be made back to Sheldon, although should it be desired that the excursion be extended, it is possible to follow public footpaths through Shacklow Woods to the Magpie Sough Tail, a distance of about ½ mile.

4.
THE ASHFORD BLACK MARBLE MINES & MILL

Conveniently situated so as to be included in a visit to the Sheldon area, the Black Marble mines of Ashford-in-the-Water may also be visited. Cars may be parked at the foot of Kirk Dale, whence the mines may be seen within a walking distance of only a quarter of a mile. Close to the junction of the Sheldon Road and the A6 main road, is the Arrock Quarry (191.694). From here the thin dark fine-grained limestone beds were quarried and taken across the road to the marble mill (190.695) where they were sawn, ground and polished to a fine black surface. The Marble Mill was established on the north bank of the River Wye by Henry Watson in 1748, who used water-wheels to power the marble-cutting machinery. The mill was in use until 1905, since when it has been used as a barytes mill and a lumber yard. Recently most of the surviving mill has been demolished, partly for road-making, and partly to provide storage and a workshop.

The Black Marble was inlaid with coloured stones in geometrical and floral designs as a "cottage industry" in Ashford-in-the-Water and many samples of this dead craft survive in local and national collections. The peak of the trade was in Victorian times, and the demand led to underground mining for black marble both from the Arrock Quarry and in the Rookery Plantation across the valley. Some mine workings are still accessible, particularly in the Rookery. In common with all old mine workings they should not be entered by the inexperienced or without reliable lighting.

A banded brown and grey limestone, known as Rosewood Marble, was worked in Nettler Dale, not far from the Magpie Sough tail, but the relics are now very overgrown.

Chert, used in grinding china-clay, has also been mined near Ashford, but there are more extensive chert mines at Holme Bank near Bakewell now open to the public.

81

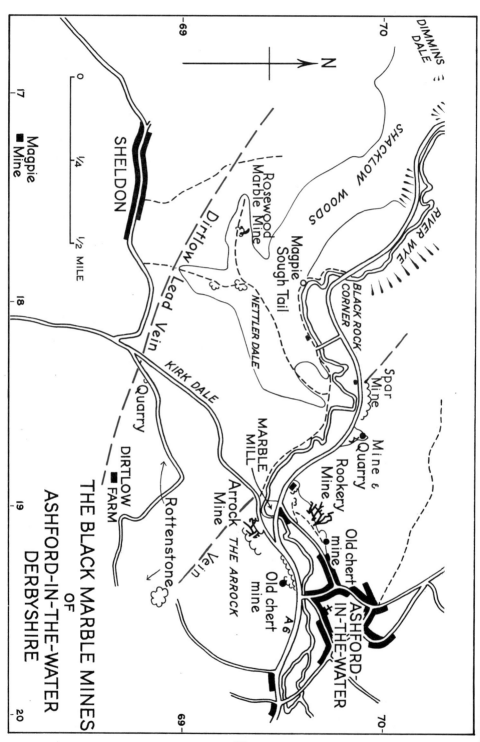

THE BLACK MARBLE MINES
OF
ASHFORD-IN-THE-WATER
DERBYSHIRE

Magpie
■ Mine

DIRTLOW
■ FARM

SHELDON

DIMMINS DALE

SHACKLOW WOODS

RIVER WYE

Rosewood Marble Mine

Magpie Sough Tail

NETTLER DALE

BLACK ROCK CORNER

Dirtlow Lead Vein

KIRK DALE

Quarry

Rottenstone

Spar Mine

Mine & Quarry

Rookery Mine

Old chert mine

Old chert mine

MARBLE MILL

Arrock Mine

THE ARROCK Vein

A6

ASHFORD-IN-THE-WATER

N

0   ¼   ½ MILE

69
70
17
18
19
20

5.
THE LATHKILL DALE MINES

2½ inches: 1 mile Map SK 16; 6 inches: 1 mile Maps SK 16 NE & SK 26 NW. Walking distance either 3½ or 6 miles according to return route.

A great deal of work was undertaken in this area by the old miners, and the Dale is particularly interesting in the unusual layout of the watercourses and aqueducts constructed to provide power to drive water wheels for pumping purposes. The River Lathkill was harnessed and a portion of its water used to drive at least three water wheels, one of which was no less than 52 feet in diameter. Steam power was also utilised and the Dale vividly illustrates the miners' ceaseless struggle with their major enemy – water. Some of the workings are still accessible but should not be entered by the inexperienced.

Cars may be conveniently parked in Over Haddon village, or alternatively half way down the steep approach road to the Dale. Care should be taken that space is available at the latter, as it is a very popular area at weekends. Two possible routes are included with walking distances of either approximately 3½ miles or 6 miles.

Proceed down the steep access road to the Dale itself. Nestling in the valley floor is Lathkill Lodge (203.661), and a footbridge leads over the river and up through Meadow Place Wood, to a farm from which the wood takes its name. This was once a monastic settlement, so too were the nearby Conksbury Grange and One Ash Grange, the latter being where John Bright, the famous 19th century Birmingham politician, spent his honeymoon.

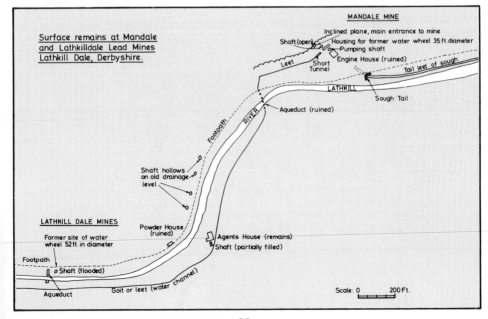

Surface remains at Mandale and Lathkilldale Lead Mines Lathkill Dale, Derbyshire.

MANDALE MINE

Inclined plane, main entrance to mine
Shaft (open)
Housing for former water wheel 35 ft. diameter
Pumping shaft
Leet
Short Tunnel
Engine House (ruined)
Tail leet of sough
LATHKILL
Sough Tail
Aqueduct (ruined)

Footpath
RIVER

Shaft hollows on old drainage level

LATHKILL DALE MINES
Powder House (ruined)
Former site of water wheel 52 ft. in diameter
Agents House (remains)
Shaft (partially filled)
Footpath
o Shaft (flooded)
Aqueduct
Goit or leet (water channel)

Scale: 0   200 Ft.

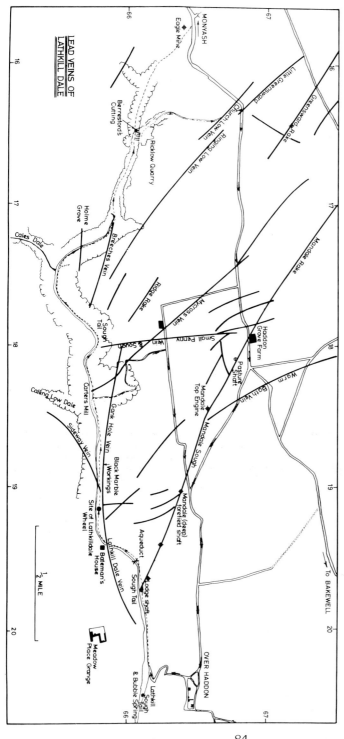

LEAD VEINS OF
LATHKILL DALE

84

The Lathkill Dale Mines

Do not cross the footbridge, but turn left over a stile and follow the river downstream. Within a short distance the path begins to rise above the level of the river, and here on the river side is disturbed ground which marks the site of the Lathkill Dale Sough, and a trickle of water comes from the collapsed sough tail (205.661), close to the impressive Bubble Springs where the main flow of the River Lathkill finally emerges into daylight.

The history of the Lathkill Dale Sough will be noted later. Retracing the route back towards the Lodge inconspicuous mounds, now grassed over, mark the positions of shafts sunk along the line of the sough. Formerly there was a shaft in the garden of the Lodge, but this is now covered over, a hand pump marking the site. The sough alters direction here and passes beneath the river at the footbridge. The Lathkill Dale Vein and Sough range in a general south westerly direction through Meadow Place Wood, though surface features are not easily traced in the tangle of undergrowth and trees. (Meadow Place Wood is now a Nature Reserve).

Proceeding westwards on the footpath along the north bank of the river, two small trial levels can be seen by the side of the path, neither penetrating the hillside for more than a few yards. On entering the wood some 500 yards west of the Lodge, a partly flooded level can be seen running beneath the path. This is the outfall or tail of Mandale Sough (197.661) extending over a mile into the hill, and driven mainly between the years 1797 and 1820, though subsequently extended. The group of derelict mine buildings which can now be seen through the trees to the right were associated with the Mandale Mine, where there were large scale efforts during the mid 19th century to pump the lower workings free of water. This mine is

reputedly one of the oldest in Derbyshire, and was certainly being worked by the 13th century.

The largest of the remaining structures belongs to the former Mandale Mine Engine House, although it is in very poor condition, being roofless, and only the 'bob' wall being complete enough to permit the former position of the machinery to be ascertained. Behind this is the hollow which housed the water wheel. The pumping shaft, now filled in, was in the bottom of the hollow. Unfortunately a great deal of limestone rubble has accumulated and the top of the shaft cannot always be seen. Above the water-wheel pit, a limestone cliff is penetrated by the 'inclined plane', now the principal means of access to the workings. This entrance should not be entered by inexperienced tourists as some of the old workings are dangerously unstable. Above the entrance the vein can be seen, in situ, between limestone walls. Outside this entrance is a small shaft, now covered, which leads via a short cross cut into the sough. Standing with the inclined plane on one's left hand, and the small shaft immediately in front, a small opening may be seen approximately halfway up the opposite hillside. This is a flue which led from the boiler house (now completely obliterated), to a small chimney, the base of which can be seen a little higher than the flue opening.

The Mandale Mining Company started to drive their sough level in 1797 and after 23 years of toil, with little return for their outlay, discovered a rich body of lead ore, followed by a second one in 1823. The first ore strike brought them a profit of £1,155 during a 26-week period, the second, somewhat smaller one resulting in a profit of £584. The Company was anxious to work the vein below the level of the River Lathkill as they were convinced a

The Lathkill Dale Mines

large body of lead ore remained, untouched by former miners who had used small hand pumps but could not exploit the vein to their satisfaction. During the year 1839, John Alsop, who was associated with the nearby Lathkill Dale Mine, became Agent to the Mandale Mining Company in succession to William Wager who had held the post since 1808. A water-wheel was installed in 1840, and this pumped from a depth of 90 feet below the sough. The wheel was of approximately 35 feet diameter, and the pumps were 14 inches diameter. In 1847 the mine was still in serious difficulties with water, and having two important levels below the sough, it was decided to install a steam engine. The engine house was constructed of limestone quarried a little higher up the dale. The engine itself was constructed on the Cornish principle at the Milton Ironworks, Elsecar. The cylinder was 65 inches in diameter and the engine developed 165 horsepower. This engine was planning to pump from a depth of 160 feet below the river, but it is extremely doubtful if the pumping shaft ever went deeper than the 90 ft. level. The Mandale Mine ceased work in 1851, after it is said, a loss of £36,000. The engine and boilers were removed in 1852, and there is a tradition that one of the pumping machines, possibly the wheel, was removed to Calver Sough Mine.

Returning to the path and proceeding westwards, following the river, the remaining pillars of an aqueduct are soon seen, crossing both the river and the path. Formerly a wooden trough conveyed the water across the tops of the supporting limestone pillars on its way to Mandale water-wheel. Despite local traditions, the aqueduct was not built in 1810, although a dressed stone bearing that date used to be

fixed to one of the pillars. In fact, the date of the aqueduct and consequently the date of the stone is 1840, but obviously the date stone has been defaced at some time and the '4' converted to '1'. There is a small clearing at this point, but within a short distance the path again enters woodland. To the right of the path, large hollows can be seen, and in wet weather a large volume of water overflows from the river into them. They mark the line of an old un-named drainage sough which drained the shallow parts of the Lathkill Dale Vein.

Shortly, a ruined building can be seen across on the south bank of the river; this is generally referred to as 'Bateman's House' (194.658). James Bateman was the Agent to the Lathkill Dale Mining Company from 1836 until the closure of the mine in 1842. Two large shafts, one immediately beneath the house, are nowadays generally known as 'Bateman's Shafts' their correct name not being known. These shafts were the site of a unique pumping engine designed by the Dakeyne brothers, flax spinners of Darley Dale. This was described as a 'disc engine', but in reality was a primitive form of turbine. The mode of operation was very complex, and the various attempts to describe its mechanical complexities are themelves extremely difficult to follow. The main parts of the engine, or perhaps all of it, were made at the Adelphi Foundry, Chesterfield in 1831. A reference dated 1833 states that the engine was working satisfactorily at that time. A head of 66 feet of water was used to supply power to the disc and a description states that 130 horse-power was developed. Here the Lathkill Dale Vein, which has ranged through Meadow Place Wood and the fields above, plunges steeply down the hillside, and cuts across the river opposite

The Lathkill Dale Mines

Bateman's House. The Lathkill Dale Sough runs along the sole (= lowest accessible level) of the vein, and during the extreme drought of 1959 was explored for a distance of approximately 500 yards downstream from beneath the House. Deep water halted progress in this direction, whilst upstream the sough was found to have been bricked up on the north side of the river. Locally, it is said that this was done after the mines were abandoned in an effort to prevent the river sinking into the sough and mine workings and thus losing a large supply of water to Over Haddon Mill. One reference says the bricking up was done in 1854.

The Lathkill Dale Vein was worked from at least 1770 to 1776 by the London Lead Company, who were possibly responsible for the driving of a part at least of the Lathkill Dale Sough. There is also some evidence to suggest that they may also have had a water-wheel working during this time, situated approximately on the site of the later 52 ft. diameter wheel. A plan, drawn in 1826, refers to "where the old engine stood", and shows a surface water course leading from a point higher up the river to this position, with the old drainage level, previously mentioned, possibly taking the pumped water away. The London Lead Company gave up working the Lathkill mines about 1776, and from that date little work was done until 1825, although in 1779 the Hill Carr Sough partners took title to several veins in and near to Lathkill Dale. The Hill Carr Sough at this time had not even reached mines south east of Alport, and never came anywhere near to Lathkill Dale.

In 1825, John Alsop and Thomas Bateman bought a part of the Lathkill Dale Vein for £25 and from then until 1842, the mine was worked on a fairly large scale. John Alsop was a lead smelter and had shares in several other Derbyshire lead mines. In 1830 a lease was obtained from Lord Melbourne to take water from the River Lathkill to turn a water-wheel, but the large wheel was not erected until 1836, but certainly one, if not two, other wheels operated on the mine. The large wheel was 52 feet diameter, 9 feet on the breast and said to be the "largest but one in the Kingdom". Certainly it was a colossal piece of machinery, working six sets of pumps, eighteen inches diameter, and said to be capable of raising 4,000 gallons of water per minute from a depth of twenty fathoms. An interesting fact is that Richard Page an engineer with the Alport Mining Company, was paid £30 "for his attendance and planning from the commencement". This appears to indicate that Page was brought in to advise whilst the wheel was erected and put into operation. By 1832 John Sheldon was the Agent, but he died in 1836 and was succeeded by James Bateman who remained as Agent until the mine closed in 1842. The wheel was offered for sale along with other mining equipment in 1849 but its fate is not known.

On the north side of the river, a little beyond Bateman's House, a small ruined building is all that is left of the Powder House, Shaft-hallows now become prominent, first on the north side of the path, and later between it and the river. These hollows mark the surface course of the Lathkill Dale Vein. The site of the large water-wheel is 290 yards west of Bateman's House, but little can be seen save a portion of the breast walling and a large water-filled hollow. The pillar of a small aqueduct can be seen on the river side, on the opposite bank, with its counterpart on the north side.

During the winter months when the undergrowth is sparse, the leet or artificial channel which conveyed the water to the wheels is well seen on the other side of the river.

The Lathkill Dale Mines

Proceeding westwardly 590 yards beyond the water-wheel installation a well-defined vein can be seen ranging north-westwards out of Lathkill Dale Vein up the wooded hillside on the right. This is Gank Hole Vein (186.658), or Gank Holes Ochre Mine, worked during the 1880's as a lead and ironstone mine. At this time it was planned to drive a long level from the Lathkill up this vein, along Mycross Vein and into the Great Greensward Mine, but the project did not live up to the early promise and was abandoned. The level was to act as both drawing gate and sough. Locally it is always said that Greensward Mine and Rake were very rich. About 100 yards east of the Gank Hole intersection is the approximate position of the Lathkill Dale Sough forefield shaft as it stood in 1782. No evidence has come to light to suggest that this level was ever extended beyond this point, but there is a possibility that a branch level was driven up the Sideway Vein by the London Lead Company, and definitely a branch level referred to as the Mandale and Lathkill Company's Deep Level was driven partway up the Mandale Vein, but no distances are known. The pathway emerges from the wood at the site of Carters Mill (184.657) and here the excursions can be continued in one of two different ways. For a short return route turn right up the dry side valley on to the minor road which on turning right leads back to Over Haddon village. Just before a junction with the road from Monyash, notice the hillocks and much worked ground of Mandale Rake (190.664). This extends both sides of the road, south-east towards Lathkill Dale, where it has already been noticed, and north-west towards Haddon Grove Farm. For a longer route, continue up the dale past banks of tufa, extensive screes, and the Holmes Grove springs to Lathkill Head Cave (171.659).

Then turn back and climb the steep path to Haddon Grove and join the road back to Over Haddon.

6.
HILLOCKS & KNOTLOW MINES, MONYASH

6 inches: 1 mile Map SK 16 N.W.

These two mines to the northwest of Monyash have extensive workings which can be quite safely visited by experienced and well equipped explorers. Although access is only possible to experienced parties, using ladders and ropes, a full description of the undergrounding workings is given so that an impression may be gained of underground features and conditions in Derbyshire lead mines. These two examples exhibit many of the features to be found in medium-sized Derbyshire lead mines. Furthermore they have a fascinating history which has been traced from at least 1670 to the latter half of the 19th century, when the Derbyshire lead industry virtually ceased.

These two neighbouring mines both worked the same two parallel veins, ranging north-west to south-east. Hillocks Mine and the entrance series of the Knotlow Mine were worked in the Whalf Pipe Vein, while the further reaches of the Knotlow Mine were worked in the Crimbo Vein. The original mine documents indicate that the Hillocks Mine also worked the Crimbo Vein, but access to these workings is not now possible. The Whalf Pipe Vein is a complex series of small parallel pipe veins and scrins while the Crimbo Vein appears to be a typical rake vein, even though many documentary references call it a pipe vein. It may be of course that the Crimbo Vein develops into a pipe vein in those parts which are now inaccessible.

Hillocks Mine: No key needed, but keep parking area clean, and do not interfere with cattle troughs etc.
Wire ladders and ropes required to visit the lower workings are 1st pitch – 35 ft. ladder and lifeline; 2nd pitch – 35 ft. ladder, 20ft. belay and 50 ft. lifeline.

At Hillocks Mine (145.672) one of the Whalf Pipes comes to the surface and this affords the present day access. After stooping through the low entrance, (now gated to prevent vandalism), we enter a roomy passage up to 20 feet wide and 10 feet high. Here traces of mineral can be seen on the roof and walls. When entered by the miners this mineralised cavern was apparently full of broken rocks, calcite, barytes and galena in a matrix of clay and sand with an encrustation of mineral on the walls. Such veins were often very rich and easily worked. Although no positive evidence exists, it is probable that this part of the mine was worked in early times, before the days of explosives.

After about 400 feet, passing under small climbing shafts in the roof and piles of "deads" or waste rock, the roof descends and it is necessary to crawl flat-out through a narrow-gap and climb down to the end of a hand-picked level. These levels are met in many old mines throughout Derbyshire. The modern name of "coffin-level" is quite descriptive of the cross sectional shape of many of them – narrow at the bottom, wider at shoulder height, narrow again at the top and just tall enough for a person of medium build to walk along without stooping. Another very distinctive feature is the sweeping pick-marks that bear witness to the fact that these levels were driven without the use of explosives. Gunpowder was first introduced into England for mining about the year 1670 at Ecton Copper Mines, just 6 miles away. Even so, many of the smaller mines would

A "coffin level" cut through limestone by pick-axe alone. Knotlow Mine. (Dr. T. D. Ford)

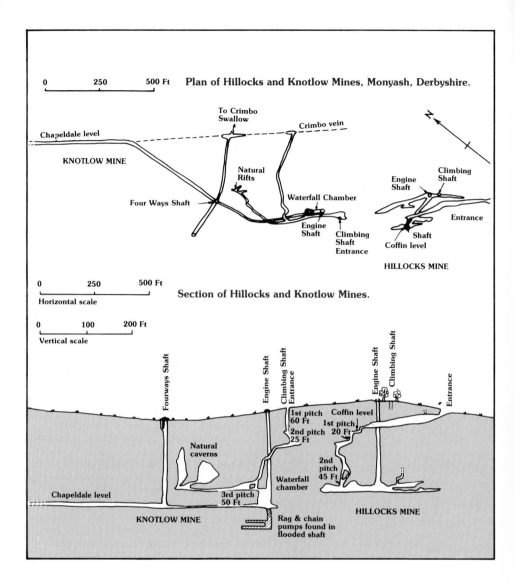

Plan of Hillocks and Knotlow Mines, Monyash, Derbyshire.

0   250   500 Ft

To Crimbo Swallow

Crimbo vein

Chapeldale level

KNOTLOW MINE

Natural Rifts

Four Ways Shaft

Waterfall Chamber

Engine Shaft

Climbing Shaft
Entrance

Engine Shaft

Climbing Shaft

Entrance

Shaft

Coffin level

HILLOCKS MINE

Section of Hillocks and Knotlow Mines.

0   250   500 Ft
Horizontal scale

0   100   200 Ft
Vertical scale

Fourways Shaft

Engine Shaft

Climbing Shaft Entrance

Engine Shaft

Climbing Shaft

Entrance

1st pitch 60 Ft   Coffin level
1st pitch 20 Ft
2nd pitch 25 Ft

Natural caverns

2nd pitch 45 Ft

Chapeldale level

Waterfall chamber

3rd pitch 50 Ft

HILLOCKS MINE

KNOTLOW MINE

Rag & chain pumps found in flooded shaft

have continued to use the traditional methods of excavation by hand many years after the new techniques were common-place in the larger mines. This makes it very difficult to date such levels. This particular hand-picked level is not of the "coffin" shape, but is only 3 feet 6 inches high and 1 foot 10 inches wide in the centre, being barrel shaped. Proceeding along this passage on hands and knees, the top of a shaft 30 feet deep is reached. This must be descended using wire ladder and rope. This too is of

the same hand-picked construction with no signs of shot-holes for gunpowder. These levels and shafts are invariably "gates" or passages from one working vein to another through barren rock. The latter day miner usually calls them "old man's crosscuts".

The shaft reaches into a series of small pipe workings which may be descended with the help of ladders to the lower parts, or "sole" of the mine, 170 feet

Hillocks and Knotlow Mines, Monyash

below the entrance. While descending, dark patches of galena can be seen on the walls, worn smooth by the mud-stained clothing of countless miners and cavers. When working here the miners would have employed "stemples", or stout beams of oak firmly fixed from wall to wall to enable them to climb up and down. In the lower parts of the mine there are large worked-out passages to the left and right. The passage straight ahead enters a waggon gate which was enlarged by the 19th century miners leaving the old man's "coffin" level clearly visible in the roof.

Turning left at the foot of the engine shaft, an extensive series of workings can be explored, while climbing up to the right leads to the base of the climbing shaft – the normal mode of ascent and descent for the working miner. Here the shaft ascends to the surface in 20 to 30 feet stages separated by short horizontal sections. Now only the first few stages can be climbed before progress is halted by a collapse. Downwards to the right leads to a series of "scrins" or small rake veins and eventually to another hand-picked coffin level which is blocked after about 70 feet.

Knotlow Mine: Key obtainable from the village food stores.

Tackle required: Entrance Pitch – 60 ft. ladder, 80 ft. lifeline; 2nd pitch – 25 ft. ladder and 30 ft. lifeline, with belay to foot of First Ladder; 3rd pitch (Waterfall Chamber) – 50 ft. ladder, 50 ft. lifeline, 30 ft. belay.

Whereas the present entrance to the Hillocks Mine is not the one the miner would have used to gain access to his lower workings, cavers still use the original climbing shaft when exploring the nearby Knotlow Mine (144.674). The first shaft is a straight 60 feet climb on wire ladder to a small chamber. While descending it may be noted that the top of the shaft is protected from any danger of earth and rocks falling from the top edges by the ginging – a drystone wall lining which extends down until the bed rock is firm and solid.

Providing this ginging does not rest on wooden beams, but on the solid rock, it is often as firm as when it was first built several centuries ago. On opposite sides of the shaft niches can be seen which were to hold the ends of the stemples, which the miner used as a ladder. In other climbing shafts in the area examples can be seen of specially protruding climbing stones in the ginging or foot-steps cut into the rock walls. Passing under a low arch, a further descent of 25 feet brings us to a natural cavern. Here the first modern explorers to re-enter the old mine found remains of wooden ladders and a series of stemples ascending a wide worked out vein. Since the miners have deserted the mine natural cave formations have started to form, producing small stalactites, rimstone pools and cave pearls. The descent is now through a series of natural chambers, some of which must have been very wide but low bedding plane caves about 4 feet high. These the miners filled with deads,

Hillocks and Knotlow Mines, Monyash

just leaving a narrow passage way through the middle. Eventually this leads to a completely natural and unmineralised series of low passages and very high caverns which the miner never entered. On the way to this natural series a coffin level is passed which, after twisting about leads to the Crimbo Vein. Here the level is blocked, but water which originates from near the natural series flows down the level, along the Crimbo Vein and is seen again in the lower parts of the mine.

From near the coffin level a further descent leads to the top of a large manmade chamber. From the edge it is possible to look across and see the remains of stemples and a false wooden floor 40 feet above the present floor. After descending the sheer drop using more

wire ladders it is seen that the chamber is at the base of a shaft from the surface fully 200 feet deep which ends in a water-filled sump. An iron pipe protrudes out of the clear water. From narrow cracks (or bedding planes) high up on the wall of the chamber two streams of water spurt out. This water has been traced to come from the natural section previously noted, and accounts for the current name of Waterfall Chamber. The water standing in the chamber was recently pumped out to reveal workings going down another 40 feet. In them were two rag-and-chain pumps, wooden hand-turned devices which lifted water by means of wads of rags pulled up a hollowed-out wooden pipe. From now on the trip is very wet and any explorer must be prepared for a soaking,

A hand-picked shaft in Hillocks Mine, Monyash. (M. Critchley)

94

Hillocks and Knotlow Mines, Monyash

which makes him appreciate the awful conditions the miners often had to work in to make a living. Just to the right of the foot of the ladder an inconspicuous opening leads to a fine full height coffin level. This level takes all the water entering the chamber. On proceeding the water becomes deeper until very soon there are only a few inches of air space available. After 500 feet a pile of boulders is reached. These are at the foot of the large Fourways Shaft down which filters daylight. It is this pile of rocks that has caused the deep water in the level. At the base of the shaft is a large cast-iron bell crank, which was used in conjunction with a small engine on the surface in the 1850s.

Three passages lead off. The right-hand branch is another coffin level, Whalf Sough, driven 1748-1755 and extending for 300 feet to the Crimbo Vein. Here is a typical rake vein, about 2 to 3 feet wide with the waste rock perched above on wooden stemples. Luckily these deads are quite safe having been cemented together by stalagmitic layers deposited by the seeping water. Here are the remains of what is probably an underground waterwheel erected about 1765 to pump water from the lower workings 60 feet below the level. The water which appears from the bedding planes in the Waterfall Chamber and flows down the level is joined by water flowing down Crimbo Vein and enters a passage which leads to the Crimbo Swallow. This Swallow took the water from the Crimbo Sough as well as that pumped up from the lower workings by the waterwheel. The water eventually re-appears at the Lathkill House Cave, 2 miles away, as the source of the River Lathkill. This is thus an excellent example of the miners' use of natural drainage for the unwatering of their mines.

Returning to the base of the "Four Ways" Shaft, the passage to the left leads to the Whalf Pipe and the base of another large engine shaft. To the north on clambering over stacked deads still awaiting haulage to the surface, a large passage is entered with the remains of truck rails on the floor. After 440 feet the Crimbo Vein is reached and the passage now follows this for a further 1,300 feet. This level is triangular in shape having been cut so as to take advantage of the narrow vein which was being followed. This passage is the Chapeldale Level which was driven from 1832 to 1844 with the intention of draining the Chapeldale Mine at Flagg Town Head, over 1¼ miles away. The miners had hoped that the narrow Crimbo Vein would "belly" out into a rich pipe vein, but their hopes were not fulfilled. Over £6,000 was lost on the project and the level was abandoned with the shot holes still to be fired and the deads to be removed.

On returning to the surface it is possible to appreciate the great battle the miners were fighting with the quantity of water pouring down the level to the Crimbo Swallow. In wet weather the lower levels are completely inaccessible to the explorer, even with his superior equipment and modern lights. It has been known for the water level at the bottom of the mine to rise by nearly 40 feet, nearly to the top of the Waterfall Chamber.

7.

THE ALPORT-BY-YOULGREAVE MINING FIELD

2½ inches: 1 mile Map SK 26; 6 inches: 1 mile MAP SK 26 SW

A little over 2 miles south of Bakewell stands the hamlet of Alport at the confluence of the rivers Lathkill and Bradford. During its heyday this small area was one of the most intensively worked mining fields in Derbyshire, and owing to its unique geological position, tremendous efforts were made to "unwater" the mines as they went deeper and deeper. Many miles of soughs were driven, with numerous branches following various veins, and waterwheels and a Newcomen engine erected. Subsequently parts of the rivers' flow was diverted down level and shafts to work water-pressure engines to pump still more water from greater depths. The most interesting facets of the mining story are thus underground, and for the most part inaccessible. The historical introduction to this itinerary will, it is hoped, provide the visitor with a fascinating background to the surface relics still visible.

The mines discussed herein lie mostly to the south of the rivers where the limestones containing the veins dip at an angle of about $10°$ beneath the shales which outcrop only a few hundred feet to the south. These in turn incline beneath the gritstone-capped Stanton Moor. Many of the shafts were sunk in shale to reach limestone at depth. Parts of the soughs were driven in shale too. Two toadstones lie beneath the limestone, and incline southwards from their outcrops around Over Haddon so that they are for the most part far below the mined areas though they were penetrated at depth in Wheel's Rake and in the Mill Close Mine workings well to the south-east of Alport. Toadstone was also reached in Broadmeadow Shaft. The limestone north of the river rises to a little over 600 feet, and to the south-east Stanton Moor rises above the shales to over 1,000 feet.

Hillcarr Sough, the main drainage level for the area, was driven under Stanton Moor into the Alport ground from a point on the west bank of the River Derwent opposite Darley Dale, about 1½ miles south of Great Rowsley. The sough-tail is still open at about 320 feet (258.637). The altitude of the sough in the Alport Mines is probably not much more than 335 feet. Earlier soughs to the River Lathkill provided drainage at about the 400 feet horizon, e.g. Shining and Alport Soughs. The arrival of Hillcarr Sough in this ground thus drained a further 65 feet or so of ground and later provided the hydraulic head to enable the water-pressure engines to drain a further depth of about 125 feet below the sough.

From Long Rake, which lies to the north of the River Lathkill, the strata dip into a trough aligned approximately west to east gently sloping towards the Derwent to the east. The base of the trough runs to the south of the centre of the Alport mining field and appears to form a focal point for the percolating rain water in the

A hand-picked level, Shining Sough, Alport by Youlgreave. *(A. E. Marsh)*

The Alport-by-Youlgreave Mining Field

surrounding catchment area. Water trickling through the joints and bedding plants of the limestone thus converged to produce a very difficult drainage problem when the pumps installed in these mines depressed the water level below that of the water-table. It was reported when the mines were working that in spite of a certain amount of successful surface work, water still sank into the mines at a rate varying from 2,000 to 6,000 gallons per minute. John Taylor, the famous mining engineer, and manager of Alport Mines in the 1840s expressed the opinion that this was the largest quantity of water ever recorded in the history of mining, though, as he must have known, this was an exaggeration.

Old documents describe the mines as being at the deepest points of a "basin heavily indurated with water". When the pumps were lifting water from below Hillcarr Sough it was at times discharging far more than 6,000 gallons per minute since it was also the outfall for water deliberately diverted down the shafts from the Rivers Lathkill and Bradford to work the hydraulic pumps.

The operation of the pumping engines was thus very much at the mercy of the seasons since during a dry summer or long freeze-up the Bradford and Lathkill provided insufficient water to enable the pumping engines to hold the water level down in the workings.

Mining Liberties

The mining liberties embracing these veins are Haddon (north and east of the Lathkill), Hartle (=Harthill) (south of the Lathkill and west of Ivy Bar Brook) and Stanton (to the east of the Brook), each with meers of 28 yards, and Youlgreave, (between the Bradford and Lathkill) with 29 yards. All are private liberties.

History

The name Youlgreave appears to be derived from the Saxon Aldgroove or Auldgroove meaning Old Mine. The word 'groove' or grove was commonplace in Derbyshire and miners were often called groovers. The earliest documents and plans which have survived go back little beyond the beginning of the 18th century. The following dates span almost three centuries:

1647 Mineral articles for the Liberty of Harthill written down at a Barmoot Court (confirmed in 1720).

1670s Old Wheels Rake Sough under construction.

1679 Reference to unsuccessful attempts to unwater a mine at Youlgreave by "wheels and tricks".

1700 Deep drainage in progress at Haddon fields (probably Wheels Rake) with water wheel and adit below water level.

1706 Articles of Agreement drawn up to drive Alport Sough, one of several early, shallow drainage levels.

1718 Alport Sough shown on a plan as having reached and being driven south in the Cathole Vein, near Windy Arbour Vein.

1740 Blythe Sough already driven some distance.

c1745 Principal veins taken by a Mr. Haley "from London". He erected a water wheel at Stoney Lee, to lift water to sough level.

c1750 Peter Nightingale drove another sough to Stoney Lee, and erected a 'fire engine' (Newcomen).

1756 Shining Sough started (particularly active in the 1770s).

1766 Hillcarr Sough started. It took 21 years to complete and by 1769 it had been driven 1,000 yards in shale.

The Alport-by-Youlgreave Mining Field

1774 A gas explosion in Hillcarr Sough injured several men.

1775-6 Relief felt in Stoney Lee as Hillcarr released large springs.

1777 Six men killed by gas in the sough.

1778-9 Stanton Moor Shaft sunk to ventilate sough, so that it could continue. (2,944 yards from entrance.)

1780 Brown Bank Shaft sunk to ventilate the sough. (3,358 yards).

1782 Agreement to drive Stanton Enclosure Sough out of Hillcarr to Stoney Lee Mines – probably never constructed.

1783 Hillcarr Sough reached Greenfields shaft. (4,218 yards).

1787 First profit for Hillcarr Sough recorded. A celebration was held for the unwatering of Guy Vein. The sough was driven north-west up Guy Vein and north-east up Old Cross Vein to Broadmeadow.

1791 Agreement with Bache Thornhill to drive Thornhill Sough, a branch level, out of Hillcarr Sough.

1801 Richard Trevithick, the well-known Cornish engineer was approached concerning an engine suitable for Alport Mine.

1802 Trevithick submitted drawings of a hydraulic engine.

1805 Trevethick's engine installed at Crash Purse shaft. (It was later moved to 'Old Engine Shaft'.)

1813 A second, similar but smaller engine erected by Richard Page on Bacon Close Vein.

1819/1820 First hydraulic engine installed at Broadmeadow (now in the Mining Museum, Matlock.)

1825 Reference to a water-wheel on Wheel's Rake.

1835 A large water-wheel was installed at Wheel's Rake.

1836 A new engine at Broadmeadow started work.
A new water-wheel at Wheel's Rake was pumping into a further extension of Thornhill Level, made between 1825 and 1835.

1839 Titles of all mines owned by Hillcarr Sough, Shining Sough and Blythe Mines consolidated to form Alport Mining Company.

1841 Tenders for a further hydraulic engine examined. The underground water-course to convey water from the River Lathkill to Guy engine completed.

1842 The main shafts had been sunk 21 fathoms below sough level and main levels had been driven in several veins.

1845 Alport Mining Company order another hydraulic engine for Pienet Nest Shaft.

1847 Serious water trouble was encountered and all engines stood idle for a time.

1848 A hydraulic engine installed on Thornhill Sough in Stanton. Another crisis due to excessive water in the Alport Mines.

1851 Alport Mining Company informed Mr. Thornhill that they would have to abandon Stanton Mines due to water trouble.
By November the engines and other equipment were advertised for sale.

1852 Mine equipment sold by auction.

1854 Final dividend paid by the Alport Mining company. A 'New Company' was formed by some of the shareholders. Suggestions in the Derby newspaper to extend Hillcarr to Magpie Mine.

1860s Danger Level extension of Hillcarr Sough being driven up Windy Arbour Vein.

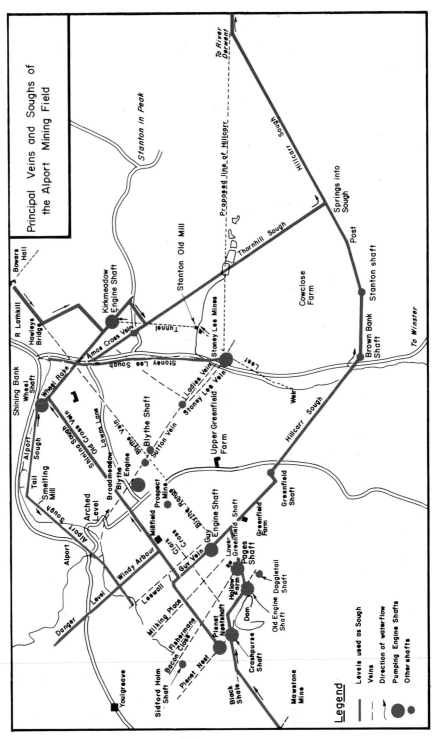

Principal Veins and Soughs of the Alport Mining Field

Legend

Levels used as Sough
Veins
Direction of waterflow
Pumping Engine Shafts
Other shafts

The Alport-by-Youlgreave Mining Field

1870s Revival of interest in Hillcarr Sough as a means of draining Mawstone Mine.

1875 Alport Mining Company ended active mining, and relied on composition from the sough. Most shareholders withdrew.

1878 Mosstone Mining Company formed to work Mawstone Mine.

1882 Mawstone Level driven along Clay Vein as an extension of Hillcarr Sough.

1891 A steam engine and a ventilation pump were at Mawstone Mine.

1893 Mosstone Mining Company went into liquidation.

1919 Bradford Vale Mining Company Limited of Matlock formed to work Mawstone Mine (wound up in 1967). Put forward a scheme to unwater the mine by hydraulic pumps.

1922 A further scheme to extend Hillcarr to Lathkill Dale and Magpie Mines.

1932 Serious gas explosion at Mawstone Mine whilst driving level in shale towards Gratton Dale killed 5 miners and 3 rescuers and thus closed the mine. Underground work was not started again.

1974 Planning permission given for underground mining at Shining Bank, north of the Lathkill-Bradford.

The dates given above serve to put into perspective the rise and decline of mining activity in the Alport field. The story which emerges is one of an industry expanding rapidly in the second half of the 17th century and striving to reach ore beneath the natural water table. During the early 18th century a great deal of effort was expended on dealing with the water problem by driving several soughs from the River Lathkill and Bradford and in the late 18th century by driving the much longer and deeper Hillcarr Sough from the River Derwent. As the miners strove to reach deeper ore the opening of the 19th century saw the development of an extensive drainage system based on the use of water pressure engines utilising Hillcarr Sough as a pumpway. Some of the 18th century soughs and the pumping engines of the 19th century are particularly interesting.

Hillcarr Sough

Started in June 1766 it became the longest sough in Derbyshire with a length of 4½ miles. The major shareholders were smelters and mine owners, Peter Nightingale of Lea, and John Barker of Bakewell. Another was John Gilbert, agent to the Duke of Bridgewater, who had overseen the construction of the underground canal system in the Worsley Coal Mines, and the Bridgewater canal which linked them to Manchester. The Worsley Mines and canal were visited by Barker, and the then advanced technology used in driving the sough was probably derived from coal mining experience via Gilbert. Apart from the unusually large size of the tunnel, up to ten feet before arching, and the use of boats for haulage, fans and a water-blast were used for the air supply, instead of relying on frequent shafts, while boring was introduced to link the shafts to the sough below. The surveying must have been exceptionally good, to intersect shafts so far apart. By 1769 the sough had progressed in a westerly direction about 3,000 feet but then instead of proceeding to Stoney Lee Mines, it turned south-west for about ¾ of a mile, to avoid driving in limestone, keeping in the softer shale in which the Stanton Moor and Brown Bank Shafts were sunk. From Brown Bank it went north-west, reaching Greenfield or

The Alport-by-Youlgreave Mining Field

Great Shaft in 1783. Close to where Thornhill sough branches north-west, strong springs were encountered and these drained Plackett Mine at Winster, two miles to the south.

The sough was navigable by long flat-bottomed boats beyond Greenfield Shaft. Though it was subsequently to be extended in several veins, the sough was considered as completed in 1787 having reached Guy Vein after taking 21 years to drive and the expenditure of some £32,000. In 1787 the first profits appeared in the Reckoning Book, and are said to have covered the expenditure on the sough within two years of its completion due to the rich ore which it made accessible. Work inside the sough must have been hard and unhealthy in wet conditions with bad air. Airshafts were few, and the explosions show that the fans and waterblast did not entirely overcome the ventilation problems.

The boaters were paid 1/2d. a day whilst the miners and pumpers received 1/- a day. The cost of driving the sough rose from 25/- to 50/- a fathom in 1769 to between £3 and £10 a fathom in 1770 which reflects increasing difficulties rather than rising wages. The wet conditions required the use of tin tubes to enclose the charges of gunpowder for blasting. To keep the sough clear of accumulated mud, men were employed to keep the water and sludge moving by means of primitive churn pumps and scrapers. The men undertaking this wet work were paid around 2/- a day, twice as much as the miners. Little wonder that the masters urged the men in their difficult task with free issues of gunpowder and candles (normally purchased by the men) and gifts of ale, rum, meat and bread. The completion of the sough in 1787 was celebrated in April of that year. The Reckoning Book shows "expenses at the rejoicings" and "bottles of rum to Hillcarr" – £36! An ox and two sheep were roasted and ale was provided by the Duke of Rutland. Some 400 to 500 people attended the celebration in spite of poor weather!

In 1791 an agreement was entered into to drive a sough branching out of Hillcarr Sough known as Thornhill Sough, later extended along Wheel's Rake to the Wheel Shaft between 1825 and 1835. Suggestions to extend the sough towards Magpie were not taken up, except for the Danger Level, following Windy Arbour Vein under the River Bradford, into Youlgreave Liberty, and the most important nineteenth century extension was the level along Clay Vein to the Mawstone Mine, in 1882.

The Water Pressure Engines

Much of the rich ore which became accessible in 1787 was won during the next decade and thoughts soon turned to deeper drainage. The low gradient of the Derwent made it impractical to drive a sough deeper than Hillcarr. The need therefore arose for a pumping engine. The economics of steam power proved to be unfavourable and the topographical features appeared well suited to the use of water power and the subsequent pumping engines installed in the Alport area were hydraulic, i.e. water pressure engines, except for a water wheel on Wheel's Rake.

The hydraulic engine is designed to make use of a small volume of water with a large fall. The principle of operation is that the piston is moved within the cylinder by water pressure instead of steam. During the 19th century seven such engines were placed underground in the Alport and Stanton Mines, all but one of them powered by water from the Bradford and

The Alport-by-Youlgreave Mining Field

Lathkill Rivers carried by iron pipes down the shafts. The motion of these engines was carried to pumps by means of pump rods thus lifting water from below Hillcarr Sough and discharging it, together with the water used to work the engines, into the Sough, or its branches.

Negotiations with Richard Trevithick started in 1801 concerning the first engine, subsequently known as the Old Engine or Trevithick Engine. During the 47 years that it worked it saw service in Crash Purse Shaft and later in the shaft near Hollow Farm. It started work in 1805. The water which powered it was carried down the shaft in pipes 15 inches in diameter with a fall of 150 feet, and this high pressure water acted alternately on either side of a piston moving in a cylinder 24 or 25 inches in diameter by means of two valve pistons raised and lowered by a rocking beam. The beam was connected to and moved by the pump rods working two 33 inches diameter pump cylinders with a stroke of 10 feet. Rods in the shaft were connected to a balancing beam at the surface. The engine appears to have worked at about 3 strokes per minute, each stroke using 416 gallons of feed water and raising rather more than 250 gallons from about 50 feet below the sough. It had been designed to work at about twice this rate and develop 174 hp. This engine stayed in service until the closing of the mines in 1852. A second engine, similar in design was installed in 'Pages Shaft' about 1813, by Richard Page who remained as engineer until 1842. But both engines acting together found it hard to cope with the water. In 1819 a third engine, known as the Blythe Engine, was installed in Broadmeadow Shaft.

The fourth engine, a single acting engine made by William Fairbairn of Manchester, was installed in Broadmeadow Shaft in 1836. The installation was difficult

as the engine base alone weighed over 4 tons and measured about 14 ft. by 6 ft. To transport the beam up Priesthill required 18 horses. Some parts were late in delivery and the reconstruction of the engine in the confined space excavated for it underground presented problems. The installation took from January 1836, when the base was laid, until the following September, but it failed in 1837.

By 1838 it was apparent that future mining required much more pumping power, and to effect this the three main companies in the area consolidated to form the Alport Mining Company, and invited John Taylor to become the manager. As at Magpie and elsewhere he attempted to introduce the 'Cornish System' of mining on a large scale, and, ignoring James Barker's suggestion to install a steam engine, he used hydraulic engines on a lavish scale to deepen the workings from 8 fathoms to about 21 fathoms below the Hillcarr Sough. Old Engine and Blythe Engine shafts were sunk to this level in 1841, whilst, by using an old engine, possibly the 1819 engine, with an 18 inch cylinder and 7 feet stroke, and old shaft, known as Guy's, was widened, and deepened, and prepared for the largest of the engines, the famous Guy Engine. This was made by the Butterley Company, and installed by early 1842. This huge engine had a cylinder diameter of 50 inches, with a stroke of 10 feet. Iron pipes carried on a wooden viaduct conducted the feed water from the River Lathkill over Alport village just above Alport Bridge and through a tunnel in the hillside (still open for a few yards) which ran first to Broadmeadow Shaft and then to Guy Shaft. Here the water descended 132 feet in 40 inches diameter iron pipes in the 11 feet 4 inches by 10 feet 4 inches shaft (now only a water-filled hollow). This column of water acting only on the underside of the

The Alport-by-Youlgreave Mining Field

50 inches diameter piston exerted a pressure of 58 lbs. per sq. inch representing a force of 50 tons on the piston. The engine was situated 210 feet below the surface and working at about 70% efficiency pumped from a depth of nearly 140 feet below the sough by working, through massive plunger (pump) rods, a 42 inches diameter pump discharging an estimated total volume of about 5,000 gallons per minute into the sough in very wet weather. The rods were of pitch pine two feet square and performed 5 strokes a minute of the plunger. A model may be seen at the South Kensington Science Museum.

By 1845 it was considered necessary to install yet another engine, with twin 24 inch cylinders and 10 feet stroke, on Pienet Nest Shaft, whilst in 1847 a further engine was placed in Kirkmeadow Shaft to drain the Stanton Mines. This was specially made so it could have liners placed inside the cylinders to reduce them from 24 to 19 inches diameter, in order presumably to economise on water, since the streams used were very small, despite long leats and tunnels.

Despite this proliferation of engines however, the water was not overcome. In winter heavy flooding took place, in summer, otherwise the most favourable season, there was an inadequate water supply from the rivers, so that in 1847 Taylor decided to pump to 10 fathoms depth, instead of 21 fathoms, whilst it was hoped the Stanton Engine would cope with winter inrushes. This was also unsuccessful, and the contemplated 12 fathom level below the sough was abandoned during sinking, and the level went off at 8 fathoms instead. In 1849 and 1850, with long droughts, the mines remained virtually full to sough level, with only a few small trials continuing.

Thus, beset by winter floods and summer droughts, with the veins small and close at depth, and with shareholder confidence declining with falling lead prices and the high costs of the Cornish System, the mine closed and was sold up in 1852, with accumulated losses of over £18,000. Indeed the mine covered its running costs for only a few months of its life and was both a commercial and technical failure, despite the fame it achieved under Taylor.

A Tour of Present Day Remains

Walking distance 4½ miles.

Forking south from the A6 road 2 miles south-east of Bakewell the A.524 road follows the River Lathkill for a mile before reaching Hawleys Bridge (231.648). Turning left at Hawleys Bridge a further 300 yards south along the A.524 road leads to a convenient parking place on the right at the Lawns Lane junction (231.646).

Looking back towards Hawleys Bridge, Priesthill, in Harthill Liberty, rises immediately to the left with a stone-cairn-covered shaft down at road level. Priesthill is crossed by about six SW-NE veins almost equally spaced between this viewpoint and Hawleys Bridge, and several shaft hillocks may be seen, the most important of which are probably on Blythe Vein, ranging from Bowers Hall (235.650) to the Blythe Mine above Broadmeadow (227,642).

Wheel's Rake runs NW-SE close to Lawns Lane junction and at this point we are standing almost above the Thornhill Sough extension of Hillcarr Sough, about 60 feet below road level. Stoney Lee Sough, just below road level formerly discharged near Hawley's Bridge.

The Alport-by-Youlgreave Mining Field

Leaving Lawns Lane junction and going south for about 200 yards on the A.524, take the Stanton-in-Peak road to the left for about 150 yards. Beyond the sharp bend a walled nettle-filled enclosure may be seen immediately to the left of the road (232.643). This is an open shaft on Amos Cross Vein. Some 150 yards across the fields to the north is a tree-ringed raised mound in front of a barn (233.644). In this is an open stone-lined circular shaft some 9 feet in diameter. It is well preserved, in spite of being situated in shale, and bears testimony to the care and skill of the miners in having lined the shaft so well. It is marked on an old plan as Kirkmeadow Shaft and is at the junction of Wheel's Rake with the Thornhill Sough branch of Hillcarr Sough. This shaft housed the Stanton hydraulic engine, which was fed by water via a level about 20 feet down the south wall of the shaft. This level led to the marshy area just downslope, where there was probably a small dam, which accumulated water from the small stream, and from a tunnel driven under the hill to Stanton Old Mill (233.639) which was fed by another small stream, and by a leat extending half a mile to the Ivy Bar Brook.

Thornhill Sough is about 60 feet below the mouth of the shaft. Beyond the shaft a branch from Thornhill Sough extends to the vicinity of Bowers Hall. Returning to the Stanton-in-Peak road a large shaft mound is visible directly across the road on the hillside. Here may be seen another open shaft on Thornhill Sough (233.642).

Retracing our steps to the A.524 and going a further 500 yards south along it we reach a layby on the left where the Brook runs under the road (231.638). A short distance along the track going up the bank encircling the layby is a large hollow. This was the main shaft of the Stoney Lee Mines, (231.637), which in the eighteenth century was the site of a waterwheel, and then a fire engine; the latter pumped water into a sough constructed for the purpose. The leat, which may have supplied water for the wheel, can be seen further down the road, as a vague depression between the road and the Ivy Bar Brook, (230.636) near the milepost. It reached the Brook at a small weir (229.634) opposite the Lodge.

Hillcarr Sough was originally directed towards the Stoney Lee Mines, but its course was changed and it passed under the A.524 about 800 yards to the south of the layby and communicated with the surface at this point by Brown Bank Shaft immediately adjacent to the east wall of the road (231.630). This shaft was sealed for safety a few years ago. Signs of a spoil heap on the west side of the road mark the place. This was intended to be the first shaft on the west side of the moor, but ventilation problems forced another shaft to be sunk, the Stanton Moor Shaft about 400 yards to the east near Cowclose, (235.630), which ran in during 1973. The Ivy Bar Brook was used for a water blast on Brown Shaft, to ventilate the section to Greenfield Shaft.

Returning to the layby, and crossing the road, follow the track north-west up the field along the course of Stoney Lee and Ladies Veins to Sutton Vein, marked by several shaft mounds and open shafts. These veins are crossed by a number of other veins, including Black Shale and Blythe, and were extensively worked from both Stoney Lee and Broadmeadow. Beyond the crest of the hill a plantation is reached, and shortly Lawns Lane is regained at Broadmeadow. The cottages here (224.643) were the offices of the Alport Mining Company, and the Broadmeadow shaft in which the Blythe Engines were placed, is by the cottages, but filled with rubbish. Shining

The Alport-by-Youlgreave Mining Field

Sough passes under Broadmeadow, and runs diagonally under the gently sloping grazing land. To the left by Broadmeadow Cottages, Lawns Lane meets the Alport to Elton road.

Turning south up the Alport to Elton road from Broadmeadow for about 150 yards a patch of disturbed ground to the right (west) of the road marks the open shaft of Prospect Mine which continued working for some years after the old Alport Company was sold up.

Continuing up the road, Upper Greenfield Farm is passed on the left, and some 300 yards further on the right, a footpath leads to Greenfield Farm, (shown as Lower Greenfield on some O.S. maps). A few yards from the road in the field next to the path is the half-open, but largely rubbish-filled top of Greenfield Shaft, reached in 1783. The post of gritstone nearby is very likely one of those laid out to mark the direction of the sough, which from here heads towards Guy Vein, almost under the Greenfield Farmhouse. The track is then followed to Lower Greenfield Farm, behind which a circular wall guards the open shaft in which Richard Page placed his 1813 engine. Further down the field are the buildings of Hollow Farm, with the filled in 'Old Engine Shaft' (219.637), where the earliest of the hydraulic engines worked, after its removal from Crashpurse shaft near the lower end of the dam. Water for these engines, and for the later Pienet Nest Engine was brought from the river via Pienet Nest and Black Shale Veins, and from Hollow Dam. A short distance beyond the farm buildings the cart track reaches a crossroads with another track which is the one running by Millfield Farm and meeting the end of Lawns Lane at Broadmeadow. This track runs through a plantation 150 yards north-east of the crossroads and here is the site of Guy Shaft where the Guy Engine worked

(221.639). It ran in many years ago and is now an overgrown depression.

Returning down the track and going beyond the crossroads the track bends to the right towards Youlgreave passing Pienet Nest Shaft (concreted over in 1967) on the right of the track (216.638). From this shaft the Mawston Level extension of Hillcarr Sough runs to Mawstone Mine where an explosion in 1932 killed eight men. The spoil heap of Mawstone Mine is clearly visible a few hundred yards to the south-west. The riverside path to Alport is now taken passing Sidford Holm shaft and several veins which have been worked under the river. Danger Level, an extension of Hillcarr Sough, runs from near Millfield Farm and passes under the river near Rheinstor Rock (219.644) just above Alport and extends under Lathkill Dale. On reaching Alport the low road near the river is taken and a small footbridge (221.645) will be seen crossing the river 120 yards upstream from Alport Bridge. Near the top of the wooded slope reached by this footbridge may be seen the arched level, almost filled with chicken manure, which conveyed water to Guy Shaft via Broadmeadow Shaft to power the hydraulic engines. The level is blocked by a fall a few yards from the entrance. The water was conveyed into this level by iron pipes carried on a viaduct over the River Bradford near the footbridge.

Downstream from Alport Bridge the south bank is in private land, and it is necessary to keep to the road on the north bank. Although it is much overgrown it is still possible to look across at the bend (222.649) and see part of the ruins of an extensive smelting mill on the hillside (223.648). This was one of the principal smelting works of the third quarter of the nineteenth century, and galena from many mines was smelted in two reverberatory

The Alport-by-Youlgreave Mining Field

and several other types of furnace to produce molten metallic lead cast into 'pigs'.

There are long tunnels running at four levels for over 150 yards along the hillside forming a complex, long flue arrangement to condense the lead fumes arising from the various furnace processes. Long flues were necessary to prevent the escape of lead vapour into the atmosphere; on the one hand this usually resulted in lead poisoning of people, animals and vegetation in the area, and on the other hand, the lead which was condensed and recovered in this way could represent as much as a twentieth of a mill's output. The flue terminates in a chimney stack 34 feet high on the hillside above the mill. J. Percy in his "Metallurgy of Lead", 1870, gave detailed drawings of the furnaces and flues and described their operation. The mill ceased working about 1875.

For those bent on underground exploration and properly equipped with helmet, old clothes, boots and a reliable lamp, the cleft 5 yards from the mound gives access to over 400 yards of sough level which runs towards the sharp bend in the road, south-east of Alport, and which may be Shining Sough. It was started in 1756 passing through Broadmeadow for a total distance of about a mile, terminating near Pienet Nest Shaft, and led to considerable mining in the 1770s until Hillcarr replaced it.

Following the river for a further 300 yards Hawleys Bridge is once more reached and a similar distance to the right along the road brings us back to the starting point at Lawns Lane junction.

8.

THE MATLOCK & CROMFORD AREA

According to local tradition the Matlock area has been associated with lead mining since Roman times. Certainly several Roman pigs of lead have been found in the vicinity, one on Cromford Moor in 1777 weighing 126 lbs.; another at Matlock in 1783 weighed 84 lbs., and yet another on Matlock Moor in 1787 weighed 173 lbs. The earliest specific reference to underground mining (as opposed to surface working) of lead ore in Derbyshire is provided by a list of mines on Nestus Side at Matlock Bath compiled in 1470. Activity throughout the Matlock area continued steadily for several centuries until the 1870s and besides the larger ventures there were literally hundreds of small mines, each producing perhaps a ton of ore a year when worked part time by their owners. In addition, fourteen of the more accessible mines have been open to the public as show caves at one time or another. Despite all this exploitation many mining remains are now inconspicuous due to changes brought about by the growth of tourism and also by recent road-widening and flood prevention schemes.

A convenient point to start this walk is Cromford Market Place (295.569) though several variations are possible, starting or finishing at Matlock Bath or Matlock. A full tour will involve a walk of 5 or 6 miles and will necessitate some means of transport back to the start. There is a frequent bus service along the A6 (Matlock Dale) road.

Nearly a mile up the Via Gellia from Cromford, on the steep hillside opposite the Pig O' Lead Inn and the mill buildings, are the Ball Eye Mines (286.574) and it may be desirable to visit these before starting the main walk. Reputedly the lead ore here contains a higher proportion of silver than anywhere else in Derbyshire, the ore from this county generally being too poor in silver to justify special processing. Up to 20 ounces of silver to the ton of lead has been claimed at Ball Eye though samples taken this century assayed at much less than this. The workings at Ball Eye are at two altitudes. Near the valley top is a spacious cave-like entrance (now badly shattered due to blasting at the adjacent quarry) which was referred to in the 1740s as "Old Ball Eye Hole Mouth" but it has since become known as Rugg's Hall after one of the mine's proprietors, William Rugg, whose house was nearby on the hilltop. The pipe veins here contain much blue fluorspar, unfortunately too crumbly to use as Blue John. A booklet published in 1661 relates how miners had "lately discovered" a mammoth's skull in a cavern apparently situated near Rugg's Hall. Lower down the slope, about 80 feet above road level, are numerous workings in pipe veins of white calcite and barytes; passages link through to a sough, one branch of which is a beautifully picked coffin gate known as Founterabby where a small thermal spring flowed until it was disturbed by quarrying in 1970. By 1630 the mines at Ball Eye were already quite deep and expensive to drain. Exploration should not be attempted now because poisonous fumes from quarry-blasting are sometimes present.

Returning to Cromford Market Place, an opening between two shops directly opposite the Via Gellia road leads after 50 yards to a small walled enclosure containing the tail of Cromford Sough (295.568) which was started in about 1672 but appalling ventilation difficulties delayed completion of the mile long section to Gang Vein at Black Rocks until 1709. Numerous extensions and branches were made to this sough during the next 120 years.

The potential of using the strong outflow from Cromford Sough to turn a water-wheel and provide power was one of

The Matlock and Cromford Area

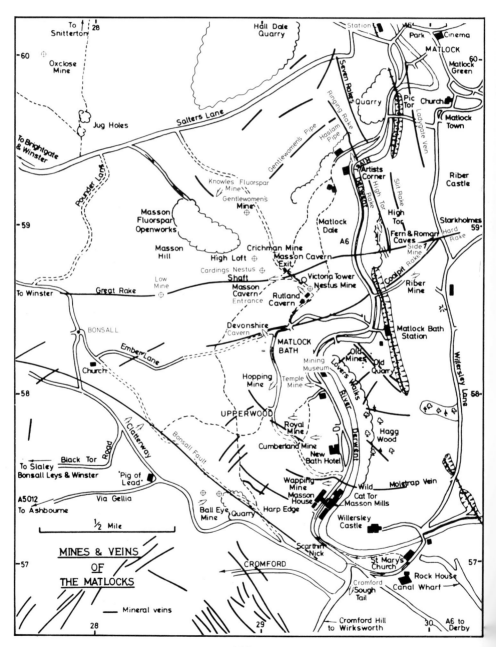

MINES & VEINS
OF
THE MATLOCKS

Mineral veins

The Matlock and Cromford Area

the considerations which caused Sir Richard Arkwright to erect a cotton mill here in 1771, beginning the Industrial Revolution. The original mill is now open to the public about 200 yards east of Cromford Market Place and recently part of it has been converted into a trout farm. Surplus water from the sough was used to feed Cromford Canal (constructed under Acts passed in 1789-91) which has its terminus just across the road from Arkwright's original mill. Subsequently Meerbrook Sough was driven from the Derwent near Whatstandwell to unwater a similar area 100 feet lower than Cromford Sough and the Arkwrights fought protracted legal disputes attempting to force the soughers to maintain the flow from Cromford Sough. In 1839 Arkwright finally had to admit defeat although by then he also owned Masson Mills where power was provided by the river.

The activities of Sir Richard Arkwright resulted in drastic changes at Cromford: houses were built in North Street for millworkers whereas the hamlet of Willersley, situated by the river east of Cromford, was almost completly razed to the ground so as to provide greater privacy for Willersley Castle, Arkwright's newly erected residence. For the same reason the track through Willersley to Matlock Bath was closed and a new route (now followed by the A6 road) made by blasting a gap through the rocks at Scarthin; during this operation over 60 Roman copper coins together with a human skeleton were found on 4th March 1795. At Willersley a large lead-smelting works was also demolished and St. Mary's Church erected on the site. The bellows at these works had been powered by a water-wheel turned by the river, on the site of the eighth weir between Matlock and Cromford. Seven of these reputedly drove water-wheel pumps to drain mines situated along the valley bottom.

The footpath past St. Mary's Church provides a pleasant walk along the river bank back to Scarthin, the road's original course. Continue northwards along the A6 road for about half a mile, passing Masson Mills, until opposite the large weir an old cobbled bridle road, known as the Wapping, climbs steeply off to the left. Amazingly, this track (recently much altered at its start when the A6 was widened) was the only road from the south into Matlock Bath until the spas there brought increased traffic during the mid 18th century. In a cutting on the left 100 yards up the Wapping path is the entrance to what is now called Wapping Mine although when it was worked for lead in the 1750s it was known as Duke of Cumberland Mine. The miners broke into a series of natural caverns ranging northwards and, anticipating their interest to tourists, a special adit entrance was made near Upperwood below the Wapping road. By 1797 it had been opened under the title "Cumberland Cavern" (292.577) as Matlock Bath's first show cave. Wapping Mine was intermittently worked for fluorspar from 1924 until the 1950s and a few years afterwards Cumberland Cavern closed. Both entrances have been sealed.

Further along the A6 road banks of tufa can be seen near the New Bath Hotel. The tufa deposit extends about 600 yards along the west side of the valley floor and was formed by a series of thermal springs which issue there, some flowing through the Derwent Gardens into the river, another discharging into the Fish Pond by the Pavilion. In the 1690s the first commercial bath was constructed and by the end of the 18th century numerous developments had resulted in Matlock Bath becoming one of the best known spa towns in England despite the thermal

The Matlock and Cromford Area

waters being no warmer than 20°C. These springs have another exploitable property: any item left in them becomes coated with a layer of calcareous matter within a year or so; various "petrifying wells" were opened but only that on the north side of the Pavilion now survives. The Pavilion itself is situated between the river and the A6 road at the end of the Derwent Gardens and now houses the Peak District Lead Mining Museum.

The Museum was set up by the Peak District Mines Historical Society, with backing from The Derbyshire County Council and the West Derbyshire District Council in 1978, as a private venture combining an interpretive centre with a depository for mining relics. A mock-up of an old mine climbing shaft and level system proves very popular with school-children but the enthusiast will find the centre piece of the Wills Founder water pressure engine more intriguing. Found in a 400 feet deep shaft near Winster where it had laid undisturbed for a century, the engine was dismantled and rebuilt in the Museum. The engine was designed by the Cornish mining engineer Richard Trevithick in 1819 and it worked on the principle of water falling from a level 150 feet above the engine being made to force down a piston in a cylinder 11½ feet long and 18 inches diameter. At four strokes per minute, each stroke raised 50 gallons of water from 100 feet below and the combined power-water and pumped water flowed out through a sough. Much of the weight of pump rods and water was counter-balanced by an enormous wooden beam and balance box and these have been reconstructed. Other tools in the Museum include picks, hammers and drills,

The water-pressure engine in Wills Founder Mine, Winster, (later removed to the Mining Museum, Matlock).
(Harry Parker)

a surveyor's dial, a stows (windlass), an ore buddle, a mould for casting pigs of lead. Some of these pigs of lead have been reclaimed from 17th and 18th century shipwrecks.

A short distance up Temple road, Temple Mine has recently been opened as an underground mining experience annexe to the Museum. Worked in the 1920s and again in the 1950s for fluorspar, it provides exposures of typical mineral associations in the walls of its adits, and typical mining scenes have been reconstructed.

Back on the A6 on the left 200 yards north of the Pavilion is Hodgkinson's Hotel, once part of some much larger premises called simply "The Hotel". At the rear of the restaurant is a short mine level, the first part of which has been enlarged and made into a wine cellar, now disused and instead shown as a novelty to patrons. Recorded in 1823 as Hotel Mine, the scrin vein here was probably found and worked during the construction of the Hotel in 1773-76.

At this point it may be convenient to make a short diversion into the High Tor Grounds where, on paying a small admission charge, it is possible to explore the Fern and Roman Caves (298.589). Strictly speaking these are not caves but very old lead workings, mainly roofless. The ore and gangue minerals have been almost completely removed from the outcrop of part of Hard Rake (the name for the eastern end of Bacon or Great Rake) and High Tor Rake, leaving deep, narrow defiles, with numerous pick marks on the walls. South of the High Tor Grounds, by the track leading to Starkholmes, is the site of Riber Mine (299.588), now almost levelled and grassed over. Started in 1952 when lead prices were temporarily high, this was the last large scale lead mining venture in

The Matlock and Cromford Area

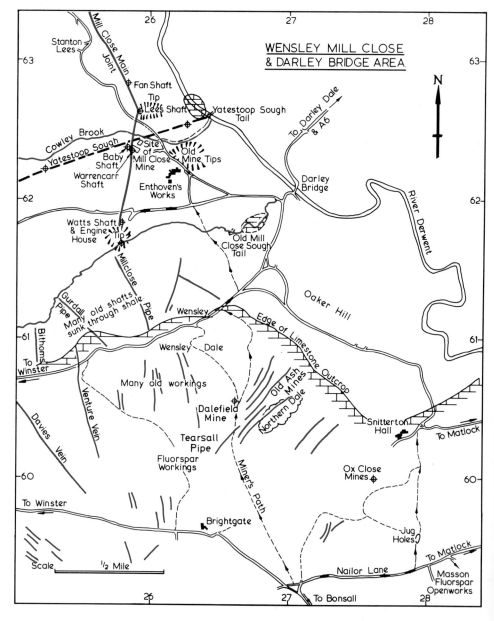

The Matlock and Cromford Area

Derbyshire. Exploratory boreholes had given promising indications and so an inclined adit was driven to work the east end of the Hard Rake complex for lead and zinc. However, old workings were found to extend much further east than had been anticipated and the ore content in the sole of Riber Mine nearly 200 feet below river level proved too poor for it to be economically extracted. Consequently the mine closed in 1959. This area has been worked during the 1820s from Side Mine using a spacious pumpway along Hard Rake from the Derwent with a "gigantic" 80 horsepower water-wheel turned by the river to power pumps which drained shafts reputedly 100 feet deep, but over £10,000 was lost.

Returning to the vicinity of the Pavilion and taking a gravel road up through the woods past Gulliver's Kingdom another show cave, called Royal Cave (292.578), can be visited on payment of the usual fee. This was known as Royal (or Pavilion) Mine during the 1950s when fluorspar and calcite were worked, largely destroying the older Speedwell Lead Mine (not to be confused with that of the same name at Castleton) which was on this site and was itself once open to tourists. Particularly large dog-tooth calcite crystals occur here. An extensive system of workings ranges beneath Upperwood to connect Royal Cave with Tear Breeches Mine (formerly the Fluor Spar Cavern show cave) and Hopping Mine, both now sealed.

From the A6 north of the Pavilion Holme Road (opposite the station approach) or any of the several steep paths lead up to the wooded grounds of the Heights of Abraham where, on paying a small charge, access is gained to the Zig Zag Walks and to Rutland Cavern (293.586) which is well worth a visit. Following many centuries of exploitation

for lead ore by means of vertical shafts, part of Nestus Mine was opened as the Rutland Cavern show cave in 1810 after an adit had been driven through a lava flow to link with cavernous mine workings in the underlying limestone beds. The new name was in honour of the Duke of Rutland, once a shareholder in Nestus Mine which yielded ore worth £2,400 in 1671. Apart from lead ore, there are spectacular convolutions of fluorspar and barytes, and traces of the uncommon mineral rosasite (copper–zinc carbonate) and the rare cinnabar (mercury sulphide). Beyond the tourist route uncharted workings extend below Great Masson Cavern. There are numerous old shafts (now covered over) on the surrounding hillside, one of which enters the lower part of Nestus Mine where workings reach a depth of 400 feet, ending in a shaft flooded with thermal water. The mines on "the Nestalls" are the first in the Matlock region to be specifically documented, being listed as early as 1470 by which time they were already well established.

Near the top of the Heights of Abraham is the Victoria Tower which gives magnificent views of the neighbourhood. Behind the Tower is Great Masson Cavern (292.587), yet another show cave and usually open at weekends in the summer. Initially Masson Cavern follows the powerful Bacon Rake (now sometimes called Great Rake) which outcrops so prominently that it may have been exploited on the surface by the Romans both here and along its eastwards continuation on High Tor. Perhaps the Domesday Book in 1086 was referring to a mine on this rake when it listed "one lead work at Mestesford". The underground route in Masson Cavern soon turns northwards along a belt of fluorspar pipe veins that have an overall width of nearly 300 feet in places. The area that has been

The Matlock and Cromford Area

shown to tourists ends in a particularly large chamber mentioned in 1676 as a "great open". The maze of connecting workings includes numerous pockets lined with unusually short pick-marks where early miners hacked out lead ore. When worked for lead during the last century, this was part of Carding's Nestus Title although recently fluorspar miners have confused it with Black Ox Mine which is the next title northwards. An incline level started from the surface in 1971 to facilitate haulage of the spar was soon abandoned when water was encountered and no further underground work has been done here.

Carding's Nestus Title and the "great open" in Masson Cavern both end at the "Hard Forefield", the northern limit of these workings during the 1670s. Here the mineralization in the pipe veins almost pinches out and the extension northwards into what is now High Loft Title (originally Black Ox) was not found until about a century later, the pipes being at a depth of 100 feet with no indication on the surface as to their range. Only one small passage is open between the two titles although since the 1920s they have been jointly worked for fluorspar on an intermittent basis. In 1779 miners at High Loft discovered a large natural cavern described as being lined "with the most beautiful petrifactions", all of which unfortunately have been stripped off and the cavern, some 150 feet long by 50 feet high, much altered by mining.

From High Loft Mine the workings continue northwards into Crichman (recently part of Masson) Title, also known as Knowles Mine after the family which owned it for a century following its discovery in about 1750. The forefield was gradually driven onwards until 1848 when it stood over half a mile distant from Bacon Rake. The pipe veins had risen with the strata until within 40 feet of the surface and were very easy to work but the lead ore content had become too low for further development, production ceasing in 1872. As with Carding's Nestus and High Loft mines, Crichman never yielded spectacular amounts of lead ore, its peak being some 65 tons in 1805. However, the pipe veins there were very rich in fluorspar, quantities of which were sold even before 1800 for use as a flux in smelting copper ore from the Ecton Mines in Staffordshire. Fluorspar extraction resumed on a much greater scale during the 1930s with the sinking of Beck Shaft near the narrow Crichman Old Founder Shaft and the working of King Mine (originally Crichman New Founder Shaft). A few years later a large adit was driven into the pipe veins further north than the lead miners' forefield and an extensive series of galleries developed in what was called Knowles Fluorspar Mine. It was soon realized that quarrying methods would be more economic and the resulting openworks ripped through virtually all of Knowles Fluorspar Mine but were temporarily abandoned before they had intruded on much of the old lead workings. In the late 1970s these activities were restarted and all the mine passages south to near Beck Shaft have been totally destroyed. An underground connection (now destroyed) between Beck Mine and Gentlewomen's Mine, ranging eastwards downhill, was forced to lead via lead workings in Old Jant Mine, Masson Sough, Deep Shaft Mine, Haslam Pipe, and Ringing Rake Sough, to emerge at the sough tail on Seven Rakes by the A6 road at Artists Corner. This is 700 feet lower than the shaft collars on top of Masson

The Matlock and Cromford Area

Hill, so the through trip (now partly destroyed) to Masson Cavern was once well over a mile in length with 7 miles of passages surveyed.

The Masson mine workings indicate a complex geological history. A mass of limestone between two layers of volcanic toadstone was partly converted into dolomite by the processes of mineral deposition. Subsequently some dolomite was dissolved away and replaced by fluorspar, with limited amounts of galena, and of barytes. At some stage underground streams wore out caves which later became filled with sands and silts from the melting ice of the Great Ice Age. Lead miners followed any available weakness in the rock, riddling the area with numerous workings.

From Great Masson Cavern three footpaths head off in different directions. That to the south cuts through woods in the top of the Heights of Abraham grounds to Ember where a turning to the left follows prominent fluorspar excavations on the range of Coal Pit Rake down to Upperwood Road and thus back to Matlock Bath; on this rake is Devonshire Cavern (290.584), a derelict show cave consisting of a steeply inclined series of natural caverns and lead workings. At Ember two other footpaths offer alternatives to that passing Devonshire Cavern, one going to Bonsall via Ember Lane, the other to Cromford via Harp Edge or Upperwood and Wapping Lane, as indicated on the map. The second footpath from Masson Cavern trends diagonally downhill, crossing Masson Farm yard (where a short sough-like level has its tail) and so down Cliff Road to the A6 near Matlock. However, for the main

continuation of the walk take the path from Great Masson Cavern northwestwards rising slightly along the flank of Masson Hill until Salters Lane is reached. This road may be followed downhill to Matlock or the walk extended by turning left along Salters Lane over the ridge of Masson Hill and soon a footpath on the right offers a diversion to Jug Holes (279.596), a gaping cave entrance first recorded on a 1767 plan of the Calf Tail Mine Title. This path carries on down to Snitterton where a return may be made to Matlock or the road past Oaker Hill may be taken to join the main road from Darley Dale to Wensley and Winster at Cross Green, just above the Parish Church. Almost opposite, across the road, a stile admits one to a footpath leading to Mill Close Mine, described later.

Instead of turning off to Jug Holes, one may stay on Salters Lane so far as the triangle formed at the junction with the Bonsall to Winster road (271.593) where the "Miners' Path" heads off to the right from a short overgrown part of the lane and descends into Wensley Dale before climbing up to Wensley village square, from which it is possible to visit Mill Close Mine.

The 'Overseer' in Gentlewomen's Pipe, Matlock. *(D. Warriner)*

The Great Masson Cavern, Matlock, formerly filled with alluvial ore and cleared by mediaeval miners. *(A. Hayes)*

The Matlock and Cromford Area

Arched Ringing Rake Sough beneath the A6 near Artists Corner, Matlock. *(M. Critchley)*

The Matlock and Cromford Area

Mill Close Mine:

From the village square, the road downhill to Cross Green and Darley Bridge passes Wensley Hall. Some 200 yards further downhill, a stile by a field on the left, known locally as "the Clouds", leads to a footpath across the fields, towards the road from Darley Bridge to Mill Close. About 100 yards downstream from the footbridge on this path is the tail to Old Mill Close Sough (265.618).

At the road turn to the left, uphill for a short distance, past old mine tips on the right, and a view is obtained across the valley of Darley, with the lead-smelting works of H. J. Enthoven and Sons Ltd., in the immediate foreground. These works occupy the site of the Mill Close Mine, enabling one to gain some impression of the extent of this former Mine property, for here until 1939 was one of the world's most productive lead mines, with a recorded production of nearly half a million tons of lead ore.

Continuing uphill, the road becomes a track and enters Clough Wood, but by bearing a little to the left (the track to the right leads to Birchover) and then straight on, a clearing reveals a valley on the left hand with a stream and the remains of mine tips that have been reworked for their mineral content in recent times. The way ahead is over mine tips for another 50 yards, along the hillside to the remains of old buildings. This was the site of the Old Mill Close Mine generally known as 'Watts Shaft' (258.618). Water was pumped by an engine situated in this building, and the large opening was not a window, but designed to allow the 'Beam' to move up and down activating the Pump Rods in the Shaft, each rhythmic movement drawing water from a sump at shaft bottom to the level of the Sough.

The tail to Yatestoop Sough may be seen by returning to the road past Enthoven's Works, and turning northwards towards Stanton. Immediately after the tips on the right the road crosses Cowley Brook. If this is followed downstream by the track on the north bank as far as the Derwent, a few yards to the north the tail will be found in a recess in the river bank (263.626).

Yatestoop Sough was begun in December 1751 with the intention of unwatering the historically rich Yatestoop Pipe northeast of Winster and other mines in that district. The sough probably terminated about 1795-1800 at a shaft on Coast Rake adjacent to Elton Churchyard over 2¾ miles from the entrance; the total cost was reputedly £30,000. From the tail the level was excavated through shale for a distance slightly in excess of 2500 yards before intersecting Yatestoop Mine in the Spring of 1766. Unfortunately the Sough reached the mine close to the shale-limestone contact, the principal ore bearing horizon lying at least 150 feet beneath and it was therefore comparatively useless without the aid of mechanical pumping.

During the early part of the 18th century Yatestoop Mine had raised 25000 loads of lead ore and this high production encouraged the proprietors to invest in the newly invented Newcomen pumping engine or 'Fire-Engine'. Negotiations with the Patentees began in 1716 but the first engine was not operative until 1719. By 1730, three such engines were at work on the mine. The 1719 engine is of great historical significance, not only being the first steam pumping engine in Derbyshire, but one of the earliest in the world.

These three early engines enabled the mine to continue working until about 1740.

The Matlock and Cromford Area

As the pipe dipped northwards, ever deeper beneath the shale cover, drainage became an increasing problem.

The failure of the long and costly Yatestoop Sough to dewater the ore-bearing beds in the 1760's resulted in the installation of two further Newcomen engines at the northern extremity of the working. These two engines were larger and more powerful than their predecessors of 50 years earlier. Both were designed by the local engineer, Francis Thompson, the first with a 70 inches cylinder engine was erected in 1778, the second slightly smaller, 64½ inches cylinder was installed in 1782 in a specially excavated chamber over 500 feet beneath the surface. Unfortunately for the mine owners neither was successful, though somewhat surprisingly the available evidence suggests that the pumping shafts were not sunk deep enough to intersect the main ore-bearing horizon of Yatestoop Pipe.

Some mining historians believe that the second engine may yet remain in the mine; the haystack boiler, 20 feet in diameter, is almost certainly still there. Several efforts have been made in recent years to test the theory, but unfortunately progress has always been halted well above the requisite depth.

Yatestoop Sough was continued beyond Yatestoop Pipe for a further 1500 yards reaching Portaway Pipe in October 1784. Here unexpected mineralisation was discovered beneath the Matlock Lower Lava resulting in high output being maintained until around 1800.

The range of Yatestoop Pipe is now largely overgrown, though the sites of several shafts can still be seen, including Old Bess Shaft (SK 244 612) the position of the 1719 Newcomen engine. Probably the most notable surface feature is a remarkably large, flat-topped walled area adjacent to the northern Engine Shaft.

Very probably this was constructed to accommodate a large horse-gin used for lowering the 1782 engine parts into the mine some 500 feet below.

Watts Engine House is now a mellow ruin bearing little resemblance to its former glory. Constructed about 1859-1860 it originally housed a Cornish pumping engine made by Thornewill and Wareham of Burton-on-Trent. It represents the initial efforts made by the noted Derbyshire mine adventurer Edward Wass to develop the Mill Close deposit northwardly beneath Stanton Moor.

Looking southwards from the engine house nothing now remains at surface of the 17th and 18th century Mill Close Pipe. Formerly several hundred acres of the hillside were ravaged by mining operations.

A protracted dispute at the mine in the latter part of the 17th century which passed from the Barmoot Court to the Court of the Duchy of Lancaster, established that the miners, whilst having an undisputed right to work lead in the King's (Queen's) Field, had no right to construct soughs in unmineralised ground without previous legal agreement with the landowner.

During the 1740s – 1760s Mill Close Mine was worked by the London Lead Co., the first to exploit the vein on the north side of Mill Close Brook. A Newcomen engine made at Coalbrookdale Ironworks in 1748 utilized Old Mill Close Sough as a pumpway. The Sough, popularly though erroneously believed to have been begun by the London Lead Co. to unwater the Hadland Mines at Winster, is still accessible and the tail can be seen some 800 yards downstream. The level twists and turns in an incredible fashion as it attempts to follow the shale-limestone

Watt's Engine House, Mill Close Mine. *(F. Nixon)*

boundary underground.

The London Lead Co. sold their interests and leases between 1778 and 1792 and little interest was shown.

For almost a hundred years Mill Close stood idle until in 1859, Mr. Wass reopened the mine and erected Watts Engine in 1860. It was a 50 inches diameter cylinder, Cornish engine made by Thornewill and Wareham of Burton-on-Trent. Watts shaft was deepened a further 20 fathoms and this engine worked until 1874.

In 1861, ore began to be raised and continued without interruption for the next fourteen years. Warren Carr shaft was sunk to 50 fathoms in 1874 and a 60 inches diameter cylinder Cornish engine named "Jumbo" was erected. This engine had a 10 feet stroke and made seven strokes per minute. The following year (1875) Warren Carr was drowned, interrupting production until 1877. In the year 1881, Lees shaft was sunk; it was deepend to 73 fathoms in 1901 and a steam winder was used until 1939, with the chimney stack still standing.

On the death of Mr. Wass in 1886 the mine came under the control of his trustees until 1919.

A new engine house was built alongside the earlier one at Warren Carr in 1889, to house two Cornish engines. One was the 1859, 40 inches diameter cylinder, with a stroke of 10 feet, named "Baby", the other a 50 inches diameter cylinder engine brought from Wakebridge Mine, near Crich, named "Alice". These two engines pumped water up an oval section shaft, from a depth of 50 fathoms and the Old Mill Close Shaft now became known as "Harvey's Engine Shaft". "Jumbo", "Baby", and "Alice" all discharged the water drawn by them into the old Yatestoop Sough at a point some 60 feet below surface and via the sough tail it entered the river Derwent.

The Warren Carr Shaft was deepened another 20 fathoms soon after the turn of the century at which time it was 70 fathoms deep. A small electric pump was installed to lift water to the 50 fathom level, where it could be drawn up by "Baby" and "Alice" when "Jumbo" had to

The Matlock and Cromford Area

stop for any reason. Perhaps here we have a hint of "Jumbo" nearing the end of his usefulness and a new source of power being gradually introduced. There were extensions made to one engine house in 1911, but to which one is not clear. A fire in 1920 burned the grease-soaked beams of "Jumbo" house and repairs were effected using steel joists.

By 1922 a new company was formed, known as the Mill Close Mines Ltd. acquiring the property on the recommendation of the late Dr. Malcolm Maclaren. Technical control lay with the New Consolidated Gold Fields Ltd. and with the new owners came modernisation. "Jumbo" was scrapped in 1931; an electric winder was installed and this shaft became the main mineral hoist. Two stand-by diesels had to be installed because the pumps were drowned if stopped for more than 2 hours. Water and the constant threat of flooding had always been a menace at Mill Close, and as the workings extended the problem grew. In 1887 the quantity of water pumped from the workings was 1,000 gallons per minute, by 1920 it had increased to 1,600 gallons per minute; 1929, 2,000 gallons; 1937, 4,300; in 1938 a further increase brought the amount to 5,550 gallons per minute. The Pilhough fault encountered in February, 1938, driving west on the 144 fathom level, brought a permanent increase to the inflow of water of 1,000 gallons per minute. The sudden inrush of water rose almost to the 103 fathom level before it could be checked and with all the available pumps brought into action, night and day, it took over a month to gain control and six months passed by before the workings were clear enough to ascertain that the ore body was lost and no others apparent.

Shortly before this event it had been estimated that the weight of water lifted from the works to the sough was in the region of 30,000 tons per day. The early 1930's had been a difficult period with the price of lead sometimes below £10 per ton, but it was estimated that 10,000 tons of crude ore had been mined per month. About this period a production record of 800 tons of crude ore and 7 million gallons of water were brought to the surface from 900 feet below ground in a day. The maximum depth of workings was 170 fathoms and the mineral deposit worked extended towards Rowsley. During this period the mine and adjoining smelter employed over 700 men.

During the latter years the old mine tips on the property were systematically redressed by passing the tailings through the modern methods of "Froth-flotation". Very finely ground lead and zinc ores were extracted which had previously been lost to the tailings dam. In dressing ore the miners of former times had washed and jigged the crude material, the dirty water being passed into a dam carrying with it material in suspension. This settled overnight from each days work and the clear water was either used again or allowed to drain off, but this soon built up into a large tip, the sides of which would have to be strengthened by adding a more solid material and often the centre region of the dam would be pumped out or taken out by hand (when solid enough) and deposited around the perimeter where it would dry out in favourable weather. This method has long been common practice, the author himself having made dams in this way, using the slimes, but only by experience is it possible to determine what pressure the wall of the dam will stand according to the material flowing into it. Although having a crust at surface it will always be soft beneath and remains slime. Dams deposited well over a hundred years ago have recently been found to be extremely 'slimy' near the centre, although

122

The Matlock and Cromford Area

the surface has held vehicles passing over them.

The introduction of more efficient treatment plant at the Hopton works of Messrs. Dresser Minerals Ltd., has enabled vast quantities of hitherto unsuitable low grade materials to be brought in from surrounding areas to be re-treated, and since 1971 the Mill Close tips have been considerably reduced by modern rapid loading and haulage methods in order to provide immense quantities of mineral required to keep this plant in full-time operation.

The years 1938-39, saw the closure of the mine with the inevitable removal of engines, winding gear and dressing plant, sold to mining concerns in other areas or for scrap according to its value. The site with remaining buildings and smelter was taken over by H. J. Enthoven and Sons

Ltd. and the smelting of lead, chiefly from scrap material, has continued to the present time. "Jumbo" engine house was demolished in 1966, and replaced by a large asbestos shed though part of the earlier engine house is still standing. At Lees shaft only the gritstone chimney remains as evidence of the site of the former mine yard engine house and winding gear, the property now occupied by new buildings for the manufacture of concrete products.

The whole of the galena output at Mill Close Mine from the time when Mr. Wass began to raise ore in 1861 until closure of the mine in 1939 amounted to 430,000 tons of concentrate averaging over 81% Lead. At present day prices this would be worth close on £100 million. The fluorspar now being recovered may well be worth more than £5 million.

A collection of miner's tools just as he left them in Gentlewomen's Pipe, Matlock.
(Richard Bird)

9.
THE CRICH AREA

Maps SK 35 NW & SW (6 inches: 1 mile); Map SK 35 (2½ inches: 1 mile)

Geologically, the Crich area forms in miniature an equivalent of the whole of Derbyshire. It is an upfolded mass of limestone a mile long and a quarter mile wide, surrounded by the sandstones and shales of the Millstone Grit and Coal Measures. The limestone is crossed by numerous mineral veins, particularly in the area around Wakebridge and Crich Cliff.

The natural resources of the Crich area have been exploited over many centuries. The area has been mined over a long period for lead ore – it has been estimated that 200 tons of lead concentrates were mined in 1782, and mining was still important in 1833 when it was one of the chief occupations of the local inhabitants. By 1868, however, operations at three of the major mines – Glory Mine, Old End Mine, and Pearson's

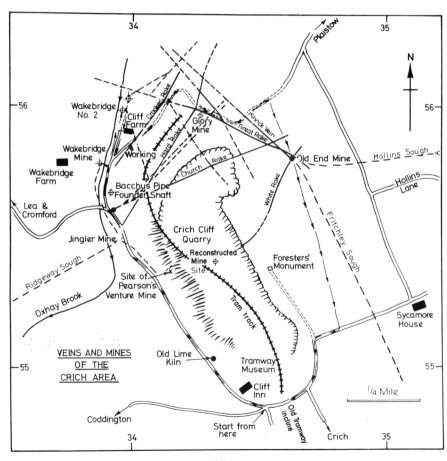

VEINS AND MINES OF THE CRICH AREA.

The Crich Area

Venture – were drawing to a close. Since that time there was only intermittent activity at Pearson's Venture, Wakebridge and Old End Mine. The growing importance of the minerals which occur with lead (baryte, fluorite, etc.) has induced periods of revival in mining in recent times – lead ore now being a by-product. Extensive quarrying in the area is evidence of the quest for limestone used for lime-burning and roadstone.

The limestone mass has been heavily mineralised with veins criss-crossing one another in a general north-west to south-east and north-east to south-west direction. A number of these veins run closely parallel to one another and may be considered to be double veins with a rider of limestone separating them. They have been given names by the old miners such as Silver Eye, Caulk, Leather Ears, Wanton Legs, Pig Trough, Shacky, Merry Bird and Kicker.

The best examples of the evidence of mining in the district are to be found in a relatively small area to the north-west of Crich, surrounding the Cliff Quarry, part of which now houses the Tramway Museum Society.

Commencing at the entrance to the Tramway Museum proceed along the Matlock road in the direction of Holloway. On the right of this road, close to the old cast-iron milepost, evidence of landslipping can be seen. A number of mines have been buried by landslips, including Pearson's Venture and Rodney Mines which were engulfed in July 1882 as a direct result of quarrying operations. At that time the quarry was worked by the Clay Cross Company which had given notice of the possibility of a landslip to the mine owners some two years previously in 1880. Following one landslip the road itself and a number of cottages were buried.

Until 1979 approaching Wakebridge, it was possible to see, on the left of the road opposite Croft Cottages, a wooden headgear in a wooded enclosure. This was all that remained above ground-level of the Jingler Mine. The headgear was erected in the 1920s, and the workings, mainly for fluorspar at that time, reached a depth of 246 feet, the lower older workings being under water, though no pumping was necessary at that time. The haulage unit used for winding ore up the shaft had a central winding drum with a cylinder on either side. One cylinder was powered by a coal-fired vertical raising boiler and the other cylinder, providing an alternative source of power, utilising compressed air. The ore was dressed on the surface where machinery was installed in buildings constructed of wood and corrugated iron, one of which (the 'jig shed') was transferred after operations ceased for use at Golconda Mine, Brassington. The headgear was erected over a shaft dating back to the early 19th century and it has now been removed. There is evidence that a number of coes constructed of stone (where the miners changed into their working clothes) existed on this site during that period. (The foundations of one such building may be seen alongside the boundary wall with the road). This shaft was formerly called Rolley and the name Jingler (or Gingler) first appeared about 1850. There appears to be some confusion between the names given to this shaft and another behind the houses on the opposite (east) side of the road, which is sometimes referred to as Lee's Shaft. The workings here were drained by the Ridgeway Sough (also known as the Wakebridge or Whatstandwell Level), which branched beneath nearby Lomas Close, one branch going north to Wakebridge Mine, the other

The Crich Area

south-east to the Cliff Side Mines, including Pearson's Venture Mine. The water from the Cliff Side Mines was said to be lukewarm. At one time an underground pumping engine was installed here fuelled by coal taken up the sough by boat from its entrance on the River Derwent, near Whatstandwell.

The sough was being driven in 1811 when Farey noted it as the Wakebridge Sough. At that time it was two-thirds of a mile long and was being driven in shale and limestone towards the Cliff Side Mines. A plan of 1829 shows a branch from the sough at Lomas Close through Rolley Shaft to Wakebridge Mine. By the 1850's it was referred to as the Ridgeway Sough and it is this name that appears in the Memoirs of the Geological Survey. In 1880 Stokes referred to it by the earlier name of Wakebridge Sough and stated that it was one mile long.

The sough was unusual in that it was a 'standing level' where water was kept at a depth of at least fifteen inches to accommodate the boats. The level of the water was maintained by a series of simple locks similar to those known from other lead mine soughs; the water was raised by slotting wooden boards across the sough between stones in the side walls. The level was approximately 4 ft. 6 ins. high and had its tail a short distance from the River Derwent, near Whatstandwell Bridge, between the river and the Cromford Canal below the saw mill. The entrance to the sough was bricked up some years ago and water now issues from a metal pipe on the river bank.

Returning to the road, turn right up a trackway by a house called Straddlestones. Proceed up this trackway noticing on the right an old hillock, built around the Bacchus Founder Shaft, which was used as a climbing shaft. The miners entered this shaft by means of a covered passage from a coe which stood nearby and descended the shaft by a series of ladders into the workings below. The Bacchus Pipe connected with the Wakebridge Mine a short distance away and was used as an access route for this mine in the early 1870s. Over a mile of levels are still accessible.

Continuing along the trackway the ruins of Wakebridge Mine buildings can be seen on the left. Here, more complete remains of mining activity than found elsewhere in the area, are to be seen. These consist of an engine house, adjacent shafts (walled round and fenced), a water storage pond now filled with rushes, and a workshop building, now used for farm storage.

During the late summer of 1967 a large shaft approximately 10 ft. by 12 ft. was uncovered between one of the walled shafts adjoining the engine house and the brook; the purpose of this shaft is as yet unknown and its identification on old plans of the site has not been found to date.

Mining has been carried out on this site since the early 19 th. century and possibly earlier. The present engine house, originally constructed of stone, was erected on the site of an earlier building which may have had a thatched roof, as was common at many mines of the period. A circular 'engine race' shown on a plan of 1829 indicates that ore was raised by a horse-gin at that time.

A steam engine was installed in 1857. Built by Messrs. Thornewill and Wareham of Burton-on-Trent, it had a cylinder diameter of 60 inches and a stroke of 8 feet indoors and 7 feet 6 inches outdoors. The engine is said to have been moved to Millclose Mine, Darley Dale, in 1889, though the mine was still in operation at this time and it may have been moved a little later than that. At Millclose it was nicknamed 'Alice' and was

126

used as auxiliary engine at this mine until the 1920s.

At Wakebridge the steam engine was used for pumping water to the level of the Ridgeway Sough, 420 ft. from the surface, and raising ore to the surface where it was dressed, sorted and washed.

In February 1863 a breakage in the pumping machinery caused flooding; tools and ore were drowned and work in the lower levels was suspended for a time causing great distress to the miners.

The engine shaft, approximately 650 feet deep, was originally sunk on a pipe vein running north, approximately along the line of the brook. During the late 1880s the miners were working a vein approximately 800 yards north-northeast of the shaft. At that time narrow rails carrying small waggons pushed along by youths, brought the ore from the forefield to the shaft bottom; illumination in the mine was by candlelight. The lower levels had been abandoned at this time owing to faulty machinery and the expense involved, the price of lead being too low to warrant the expense.

The mine has been worked intermittently this century mainly for fluorspar, with some baryte, calcite and lead being obtained. During the period 1921-31 between 5 and 18 men were employed, not more than nine underground and more usually five. During the last period of working from 1945 to the early 1950s no more than five men were employed at one time. Mining operations during this period were undertaken from Wakebridge No. 2 Shaft situated alongside the brook beyond Cliff Farm.

At the time when the Engine House was built in the mid 19th. century up to 42 miners were employed. The men were paid 2s. 6d. (12½p) per day for an eight hour shift. The Agent of the Mine,

James Elce, received £55 per annum. The mine was sufficiently large to employ such tradesmen as carpenters and a blacksmith.

Returning to the old trackway and proceeding towards Cliff Farm, the remains of a series of dams can be seen on the left along the course of the brook. The water from these dams was used for washing the ore at the mine and was piped to the Jingler Mine when it was working during the 1920's.

A short distance from the footpath is the site of Wakebridge No. 2 shaft, now concreted over. It was from here that operations were undertaken during the last period of working when considerable quantities of fluorspar were obtained from old workings. Two levels were worked, one at 168 feet and a lower one at 146 feet. In 1952 the miners were working near a point where the west-north westerly Great Vein reaches the western margin of the limestone inlier; the Hazelhurst Vein which intersects the same ground was also worked. The shaft was equipped for skip-hoisting with an electric hoist and diesel driven compressor. (Approximately 25 yards south of Wakebridge No. 2 shaft there was another shaft, now concreted over and at present covered with top soil. Mr. C. Thorpe, of Cliff Farm, reported that – "the shaft was surmounted by a chimney and connected to Wakebridge No. 2 shaft by means of a short level. This was possibly a ventilation shaft along the line of the vein").

Please Note: The Engine House of Wakebridge Mine and the shaft of Wakebridge No. 2 are both on Private Land – the landowner will gladly give permission to visit these sites if you enquire at Cliff Farm before you stray off the footpath.

Retracing the route to where the old trackway forks, ascend a hill, passing a present-day working for fluorspar with its

The Crich Area

attendant machinery on the right.

Continue up the track, circling an old shaft hollow, the track passes alongside a mining venture commenced in 1967 and then worked intermittently until 1977 by an incline (Smith's Adit) driven into the Glory Vein. Following the track, which soon passes over the Tramway Museum tram-line, near the top of the hill the site of Glory Mine is reached on the right, marked distinctively by the iron headgear set over the shaft. Glory Mine has been worked intermittently for at least 150 years; firstly for lead and later for fluorspar. Good examples of banded vein materials may still be obtained along this part of the route.

The mine is said to have been very remunerative, the lowest workings being at a depth of 810 feet. The toadstone which was encountered at a depth of 180 feet was found to be approximately 60 feet thick. In common with other veins in the area they were said to be less productive at depth. In the mid 19th. century the shaft was 480 feet deep with six or eight wagon ways.

As with most mines in Derbyshire, disputes often figure in the records. Luke Allsop, the Barmaster in the second half of the 19th. century recorded in his diary for May 7th 1870 that a riot occurred between two factions of dissatisfied miners over the working of Glory Mine and that they damaged much property; he imposed fines on each miner of 3s. 4d. (17p) which they duly paid. Six months previously he had imposed a fine of £3.9s.0d (£3.45p) on a miner after finding him guilty of practically cutting through the winding rope thereby endangering life.

The iron headgear at Glory Mine has survived from a period of working in the 1950s, when the "cage" was a torpedo-shaped steel cylinder!

Just past Glory Mine the track veers left and follows the line of the wall. On reaching the stone stile set in the wall on the right, climb over and cross the field, following the line of stiles.

In a short distance an area is reached that was, until recently (1981), dominated by the ruins of the engine house at the Old End Mine on the Great Rake. The spoil heaps have been removed and the area grassed over – removing all traces of mining activity at Old End, which was last worked in the 1940s.

The main shaft at Old End reached a depth of 912 feet and was one of the deepest shafts in Derbyshire and the deepest shaft sunk entirely in limestone. The mine was drained by the Crich Sough (or Fritchley Level) which entered the shaft at approximately 420 feet from the surface. It drains into a brook at Fritchley two miles south-southeast and the arch at its outflow bears the date of 1753. It was driven to unwater a mining title called Hollins Sough Lead Mines in the Parish and Manor of Crich.

An undated plan, possibly of the 1840s, indicates the size of the mining operations at that time for surface buildings, in addition to the engine house, included a whimsey (or winding engine), an ore house, a blacksmith's shop, a reckoning house, and a store shed, of which little now remains.

Mining is said to have ceased in 1864 due to diminishing output and the poorness of the veins at depth and the mining plant was offered for sale. The Barmaster, however, recorded in his diary for May 1867 that the company owning the Old End Mine had decided to erect machinery for clearing water out of the lower levels which had been abandoned for some time owing to litigation over disputes arising amongst the shareholders, which had been settled out of Court. Work at the mine proceeded and in 1873 the

The Crich Area

discovery of a huge cavern is recorded. In September 1879 the owners decided to start to withdraw the pumping gear and prepared to abandon the mine owing to rising costs and the refusal of the Wakebridge Mine owners to pay their agreed share of the expenses. Less than a month later the miners at the Glory Mine, a quarter mile away, found the lower level of the mine flooded due to the withdrawal of pumping machinery at the Old End Mine. The lower levels of the Wakebridge Mine were abandoned six months later in May 1880. The decline in the price of lead and the rising costs were taking their toll of the industry.

In 1908 Drabble Brothers of Matlock took possession of the Mineral Title of Old End Mine with all veins, meers of ground and rights and privileges belonging thereto as well as the Glory Mine and other mines on Crich Cliff. A period of revival of mining activity ensued for a few years.

The last period of mining activity took place in the 1940s when fluorspar was being sought. At that time the main shaft was re-opened to a depth of 300 ft. but the workings were found to be in poor condition. The shaft has since been filled with debris and only a deep hollow now remains. Open cuts and shallow shafts on Church Rake and the eastern part of Great Rake were made at that time. Good coarse-grained fluorspar was obtained from a shaft on Great Rake, 125 ft. deep, approximately 175 ft. west-north-west of the main Old End shaft.

From the Old End Mine follow the footpath to Crich passing below the monument to the Sherwood Foresters to be seen at the crest of the hill on the right. On reaching the road turn right and return to the Tramway Museum.

At Wakebridge, half-way along the tram track of the Tramway Museum, a typical lead mine site has been constructed by members of the Peak District Mines Historical Society from materials salvaged from various lead mining sites in Derbyshire. A buddle, climbing shaft, drawing shaft with stowes and kibble, adit, miner's coe, crushing circle and bole hearth have been constructed. Also to be seen are a jaw crusher, roll crusher, jig, logwashers, meerstones and water pump. A small museum, housed in a converted work-shop tram, contains mineral specimens, fossils, old mining tools, plans, etc. Demonstrations of mineral separation are also given using a Wilfley separating table.

Access to this display is provided by the Tramway Museum – alight from the tram at Wakebridge.

10.
CARSINGTON PASTURES, BRASSINGTON

2½ inches: 1 mile, Map SK 25; 6 inches: 1 mile Maps SK 25 SW & SE. Walking distance – 5 miles.

The mines on the Pastures:

An undulating grassy upland marks the southern boundary of the Derbyshire lead mining field. Somehow it has partly escaped the Enclosures Acts and is largely devoid of stone wall, and for this reason it has retained the name of Carsington Pastures. Though only 2½ miles from the mining centre of Wirksworth little is known of the detailed history of the ramification of workings and veins. The walk described below can thus only give a limited view of the intense activity which has taken place here in the past. The route is roughly in the form of a square with sides a mile long, bounded by the villages of Brassington and Carsington on the south, and by the minor road between Wirksworth and Brassington on the north. Last worked on any scale were the Nickalum and Great Rake Mines, both producing barytes in 1919. The nearby Condway Mine was worked as recently as 1940-43 and the Golconda Mine finally ceased work in 1953 after over two centuries of intermittent activity. Though the recent workings was for barytes, all had been important lead producers earlier. Many of the older workings still have ruined coes where the miners changed their clothes, and there are numerous open shafts.

There are also two small caves; one in Harborough Rocks yielded Roman and British relics whilst the other, on Carsington Pastures, could be the one of which Daniel Defoe wrote in 1731 on visiting the Wirksworth area, he rode out to see the lead mines and: "We were agreeably surprised to see a hand, and then an arm, and quickly after a head, thrust up out of the very groove we were looking at . . . . this subterranean creature . . . was a most uncouth spectacle, clothed all in leather . . . for his person he was lean as a skeleton, pale as a dead corpse, his hair and beard a deep black, his flesh lank, and as we thought something of the colour of the lead itself". Defoe also described visiting a miner's wife and five children who lived happily in "a natural opening in the rock, wherein her husband had been born. The chamber within was divided by a curtain, had shelves with earthenware, pewter and brass. A hole in the roof served as a chimney, and she had a few pigs and cow enclosed outside . . . She earned, when she could, a few pence per day, washing ore". The cave wherein this mining family resided has usually been taken to be Harborough Cave, which is so much better known, but if the cave on Carsington Pasture is examined with Defoe's account in mind, it could equally well be the place he visited.

A good starting point for the walk is Brassington (232.544), a typical Derbyshire mining village although now the main occupation is agriculture. The village itself has some very interesting buildings and a fine old church. "Branzincton" was listed in the Domesday Book. It is uncertain when mining first started in this area, but by 1683 there was enough ore being produced to warrant a Deputy Barmaster in the village.

From Town Street the public footpath to Carsington climbs eastwards across the fields to the western edge of Carsington Pasture. After passing through the last stile onto the open grazing land, turn right along the wall where there is a rewarding view of Brassington Village, the church and the uplands behind.

Proceeding up the path, just below the crest of the hill two features astride the path may be seen: on the left is an old crushing circle with some track stones still

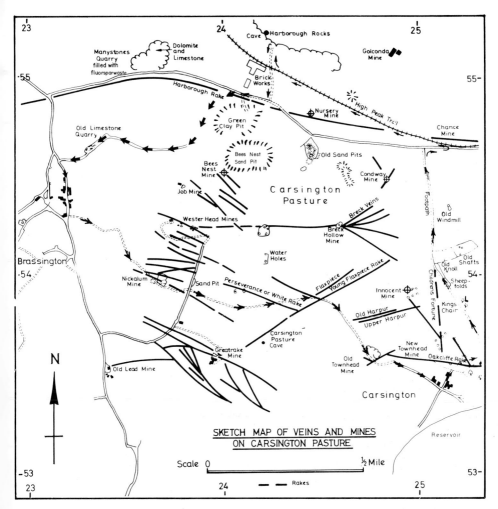

Within the map:

Manystones Quarry filled with fluorsparwaste

Dolomite and Limestone

Cave — Harborough Rocks

Golconda Mine

Brick Works

Harborough Rake

High Peak Trail

Nursery Mine

Old Limestone Quarry

Green Clay Pit

Chance Mine

Bees Nest Sand Pit

Old Sand Pits

Bees Nest Mine

Condway Mine

Job Mine

Carsington Pasture

Old Windmill

Wester Head Mines

Breck Veins

Breck Hollow Mine

Old Shafts

Old Knoll

Brassington

Water Holes

Sheepfolds

Nickalum Mine

Sand Pit

Perseverance or White Rake

Flaxpiece

Young Flaxpiece Rake

Innocent Mine

Kings Chair

Old Harpur

Upper Harpur

N

Carsington Pasture Cave

Greatrake Mine

New Townhead Mine

Oakcliffe Rake

Old Lead Mine

Old Townhead Mine

Carsington

Reservoir

SKETCH MAP OF VEINS AND MINES
ON CARSINGTON PASTURE

Scale 0 — ½ Mile

- - - Rakes

---

present though the centre stone is missing. Below this to the right of the path is an old settling pond. Where the path begins to level out the gaunt ruins of the Nickalum Mine buildings are ahead (237.540). The buildings are of comparatively recent origin and a concrete cap now covers the main shaft. This shaft is reputed to have "three turns", each of 70 feet, which would give an approximate depth of 200 feet. The Geological Survey Memoirs note the depth as 10 fathoms (60 ft.) but this would not warrant an engine, and may be a misprint. As late as 1919 the Nickalum or Old Brassington Mine was worked for small amounts of caulk, but no galena was being produced.

The mine is said to be in a pipe running west of north, with the strata forming a dome rich in lead, which at one time produced ore to the value of £13,000 in two years. With the exception of the Great Rakes Mine, Nickalum has the only engine house on the Pasture. In 1891 lead was still being produced, a measurement of 35 loads 3 dishes being recorded, but by 1895 no more than five loads were measured for the whole year.

Leaving Nickalum Mine the path curves eastwards and downhill into Wester Hollow a picturesque amphitheatre ringed with limestone outcrops and old lead workings. Descending the path, on the left at the head of the hollow are the Wester

Carsington Pastures, Brassington

Head Mines (239.542) scattered among the rocks at the head of the cart track. Some of these were sunk to a depth of 18 to 30 fathoms in white sand and were worked for cerussite (otherwise known as white lead ore). This is a feature of the area, and such ore has been worked for centuries, sometimes from open sand pits. Occasionally the "old man" following veins in the limestone has come across pockets of sand and white ore underground, but usually the sands and fireclays have been dug out from open pits for use in refractory brick making.

To the south across the hollow, is the site of the Great Rake Mine (240.536) now only a number of low walls and concrete engine beds. A few years ago the wooden headgear on the main shaft could be seen silhouetted against the sky, but old age and vandals led to its downfall in 1961. The earliest known date for the Great Rake Mine being worked is 1735. The "old man" worked to a depth of 70 fathoms and in 1919 workings went to 50 fathoms, when mostly barytes was being produced, some from a vein varying in width from 4 to 11 feet.

Following the path downhill, some old sand quarries can be seen at the side of the cart rack in the bottom of the hollow. On reaching the cart track, go straight across and follow the footpath up the other side of the hollow, and pass slightly to the left of the clump of trees on the skyline. The route now lies through heavily worked country, with innumerable shafts, so care should be exercised and it is advisable to watch where you are putting your feet.

Climbing the slope east of Wester Hollow, Perseverance Rake or White Rake lies parallel and a few yards to the left. On reaching the brow of the hill, rough worked ground extends in all directions, and the lines of the rakes can be traced by the lines of grass-covered mounds of old spoil heaps along their length. The site of Great Rake Mine presents itself from a different angle half a mile away on the right. Roughly 300 yards east of the ruins a concealed hollow has the hidden entrance to Carsington Pasture Cave (241.536). Carsington village can now be seen ahead. As the path descends it crosses the line of White Rake (also known once as Blackbird or Engine Rake) (243.538). This rake runs west to east for approximately 500 yards and according to Farey was being worked for white ore cerussite about 1811. There are a number of shafts on this rake and like most others in the area the stonework is still sound, a testimony to some unknown long dead craftsmen!

As the path joins the cart track at the bottom of the slope there are three shafts alongside the track on a line of workings known as Dowsithills. Extending up the hillside on the left of the cart track are the twin parallel rakes of Flaxpiece Rake, the Young Flaxpiece worked originally for lead, later for barytes. These rakes are dotted with many shafts and remains of coes, plus some overgrown remains which appear to have been crushing sites, settling dams etc. Barbed wire fences off some of the more dangerous shafts.

Many of the shafts in the area have typical Derbyshire mining names such as Old Horse, Beardsley Founder, Old Harpur, Colt, Appletree Swang, Sing-a-Bed, etc. The cart track is now confined between the steep shoulder of the pastures and a stone wall on the right. Just before the first of two quarries on the left, the twin veins of Old Harpur and Upper extend up the hillside. At the second old quarry (248.536), the workings of the Townhead Mine (1811) cross under the track. The workings of New Townhead (1805'1845)

Carsington Pastures, Brassington

lie under the hillside above the first houses of the village, which comes into sight round the corner. Continuing down the lane past the houses, it joins the road at a right angled bend. If a visit to the church or the Miners' Arms is desired, go straight on down the road.

To continue round the pastures, take the path up a narrow walk between the houses at the point where the lane joins the bend in the road. Reaching the gate at the top of the gardens the path turns right climbing uphill to the top of the wood on the right. A few yards to the left of the path are five shafts on the line of Oakcliffe (=Yokecliffe) Rake, which continues to Nursery End Mine on the right of the path by the stone wall (253.536). The Nursery End Mine was producing calamine (zinc carbonate) and lead prior to 1815. On the left, in line down the hillside are the four shafts of the Cow and Calf workings.

On reaching the corner of the wood, turn sharp left and follow alongside the wall uphill to the King's Chair and Old Knowle Knoll. The King's Chair (253.539) is a crag of dolomite limestone, of which the upper part has been artificially hollowed out into the shape of a throne, probably as a late 18th century pseudo-antiquity or folly. Note the rough nature of the ground on the left, again due to past mining activities, with many shafts still present. The biggest complex of workings bears the name of "Children's Fortune" while further to the left, west of King's Chair is a cluster of shafts of the Innocent Mine (250.538). This mine was working in the late 18th century and Wm. Duesbury of the Crown Derby porcelain works bought an interest in the mine for the "china clay" deposits about 1770 until his partnership lapsed in 1826. A hard white clay, halloysite, occurs in some of the sand pits and it was apparently mistaken for china clay in the 18th century.

The path continues along the side of the wall to the road, passing on the right the remains of an old windmill in a field.

Just before reaching the road the barbed wire fence on the left encloses the Condway Mine (248.545) worked to a depth of 140 ft. in the 1940s for barytes from a vein in dolomitized limestone, with many cross joints. Before this the mine was working in 1877 but only 7½ dishes of ore were recorded by the Barmaster.

This was apparently the last of the ore (apart from a small amount of 1879) for in November 1906 the barmaster served notice to work, and in December of that year the mine changed hands. The barmasters' records did not show any ore production from this new management.

Passing the Condway Mine, a metalled road is reached. Cross the road, and two stiles give access to the High Peak Trail on the old Cromford and High Peak Railway line. Here a short diversion to the right (note the old Chance Mine workings on the left) gives a view down the old Hopton Incline, otherwise turn left for Harborough Rocks and Brassington, with modern mill buildings on the site of the Golconda Mine coming into view on the right. This mine, one of the most extensive in Derbyshire, has been worked intermittently since at least the 18th century, and possibly earlier, until 1953 and to a depth of 420 ft. There are some 3 miles of galleries on an old mine plan, and the workings encountered several large caverns. On a recent exploration one of these was found to have written in smoke on the wall "I. Rawlinson, 1777", presumably a former miner, but the signatures of "Henry VIII" and "King Tut B.C.19" were not thought to be genuine! Access to the mine is no longer possible.

Walking along the trail the escarpment of Harborough Rocks is now

Carsington Pastures, Brassington

ahead on the right, whilst on the left the
chimney-like ruins of Breck Hollow Coe
(246.543) can be seen on the pastures.
This coe is one of the few still remaining
which have the recessed inner corners of
the walls said to be built that way to
deceive the barmaster on the amount of
ore present. The Breck Mine shafts (and
there are at least ten) were sunk near the
intersection of several veins running north-
west and north-east. The early history is
obscure, but ore was still being produced
in small quantities around 1880. Barytes
was also produced at a later date.

Another few minutes walk brings
you to the brickworks where a footpath
crosses the trail for Harborough Rocks and
cave. The climb to the top is well worth the
effort, giving an excellent view in all
directions, including the former sand pits
near the brickworks, now filled with waste
from Dresser's fluorspar processing plant at
Hopton. Descending from the rocks go
straight across the trail, and turn right at
the road. Here the road passes close
to silica sand workings, of interest to
geologists on account of the fossilized
Sequoia wood in the refractory clays, and
to the cover of boulder-clay deposited by
the glaciers of the last Ice Age. The silica
sands are taken to the brickworks below
Harborough Rocks for firing. In a few
yards there is a track to a quarry on the
left which is still working for sand on the
site of the Bees Nest Mine. There was a
shaft 22 fathoms deep and the mine was
worked for barytes in 1919. A small
amount of ore (1 load 7 dishes) was
measured by the barmaster in 1889 but
one would expect the mine to be much
older than this.

Just beyond the brickworks take
the public footpath just past the quarry
track (signposted Brassington) across old
mined ground down to the village.

11.
STONE EDGE CUPOLA

2½ inches: 1 mile Map SK 36; 6 ins. 1 mile Map SK 36 NW. Grid Reference: SK 334.670.

Of all the smelting sites which have operated in Derbyshire, the Stone Edge Cupola, near the junction of the Ashover – Chesterfield (A632) and Darley Dale – Chesterfield (B6015) roads, is the most imporant and best preserved site. The cupola is scheduled as an Ancient Monument, whilst its chimney is the oldest free-standing industrial chimney in Britain, dating from about 1770 or even a little earlier; it is now listed in the Guinness Book of Records.

The site is on the high gritstone moorlands, to the east of the mining area of the limestone, and 2½ miles north-west of Ashover at SK 334670, and is easily located by the tall square-built chimney at the centre of the site. This somewhat barren spot was chosen because the process gave off fumes and poisoned both vegetation and cattle. The two roads to the site, which are still known as Lead Lane and Belland (=lead poisoned) Lane, led from the formerly important lead-mining areas of Winster and Ashover, whilst Chesterfield was on the main lead-marketing route to Bawtry, Stockwith, and Hull, by road and later by canal.

The cupola or reverberatory furnace was introduced to Derbyshire about 1735-37, almost simultaneously by the London Lead Company and by the Bagshawe and Twigg families. In this type of furnace the fuel, coal, was burned in a grate separated by a small wall or bridge from a saucer-shaped hearth in which the lead ore was placed, so as to avoid contamination. Flames from the fire 'reverberated' from the low arched roof of the furnace, causing the lead to separate from the waste or slag, and then passed via a flue to the tall chimney which provided the draught. The slag was either raked or drawn off, whilst the lead was caused to run into a 'pot' at the front of the furnace. In the latter phases of the site's use, the flues were extended so as to cool and condense the lead 'fume' or vapour which came off with the gases. Unlike the ore-hearth which the cupola superseded, a bellows was not needed, but at Stone Edge there was also a slag mill, somewhat akin to a blacksmith's hearth, used to resmelt the cupola slag, so that the adjacent dam was built to provide water power for the bellows. The mill would probably be used at intervals, thus allowing the dam to fill again from the rather small catchment area.

The features of the site still visible today show a complex situation owing to two, probably three, stages in the development of the works, during which the site of the furnaces was changed. The first reference to the site is for 1771 and, though the works were described by John Farey as rebuilt about 1811, the furnaces were still sited in a barn-like building just south of the tall chimney, where traces of an oblong platform can still be seen. Later furnaces, perhaps in the 1830's, were resited at a lower level, at which time the chimney was probably raised also, to provide increased draught when the flues were constructed. There appear to have been two furnaces east of the chimney, and one or two more close to the small enclosed garden which must have been in use in the 1850's. At that date an entirely new process was introduced, probably the Spanish Slag Hearth, since the operator had recently returned from Spain. The ramp at the small garden probably gave access to the Spanish slag hearth, with nearby the base of a chimney which may have served a boiler for a steam engine providing an air blast. A maze of flues connected furnaces to the main chimney which was divided into two internally by a

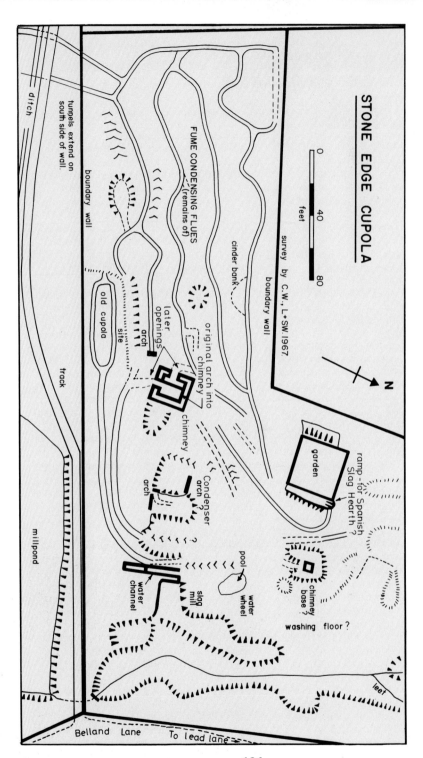

STONE EDGE CUPOLA

survey by C.W., L+SW. 1967

0 — 40 — 80
feet

N

ditch

tunnels extend on south side of wall.

boundary wall

old cupola site

FUME CONDENSING FLUES (remains of)

cinder bank

boundary wall

later openings

arch

original arch into chimney

chimney

arch

Condenser arch ?

garden

ramp - for Spanish Slag Hearth ?

track

water channel

slag mill

water wheel

pool

chimney base ?

washing floor ?

millpond

leet

Belland Lane   To lead lane

The oldest industrial chimney in Britain: at Stone Edge cupola, built about 1770.
(H. M. Parker)

Stone Edge Cupola

brick partition: parallel flues and condensers slowed the fumes down and allowed dust and vapour to settle on the walls and floor. Entrances allowed access for the precipitate to be removed for resmelting. In the last phase of operation flue openings were made on two sides of the chimney but these have now been blocked off during restoration to improve stability; only the arched original opening is visible.

There are large quantities of furnace debris on the site. Furnaces were made of gritstone, lined with firebrick and sealed with fireclay and slag. Slags found are mainly greyish, but some appear rich in iron – but the absence of large heaps probably indicates the bulk of material was carted away, probably in the 1870's when Meerbrook Cupola specialised in slag treatment. Fume deposits can be found in the flues, whilst large quantities of cinder and ash are found over the flues to the west of the chimney.

The works were probably first built by Thornhill and Twigg, who had considerable interests at Ashover and Winster, including another cupola at Kelstedge, Ashover. For some time prior to 1789 the works was owned by John Twigg and Humphrey Winchester, whose business in that year failed, so that Twigg's Derbyshire and Welsh interests had to be hurriedly sold. It then passed into the hands of Barker and Wilkinson, who operated several cupolas in Derbyshire, and who produced up to 500 tons annually at Stone Edge, until in 1807 they moved their operations to their newly acquired works in Stoney Middleton. It was then occupied by Sykes, Milnes and Co. Milnes was a smelter who came from a long-established family of lead merchants in Ashover, whilst Sykes was head of one of Hull's best known shipping houses, presumably supplying both capital and market for the firm. In 1811 the works were described by John Farey as having the most improved cupolas in Derbyshire; Farey also gave a full account of the techniques of operation.

William and Charles Milnes appear to have used the site about the 1830's, but it was described as unused for about 15 years in 1849, except for a short while when a 'man named Pasco came from Cornwall'. Of Pasco nothing is known except that a Charles Pasco from Cornwall married a Sheldon girl, and lived at Sheldon in 1851, though at the time he was probably working away from home as a coal miner (he was probably one of the Cornish Magpie miners). Pasco stayed only a little while, but in 1848-9 the works were taken over by James Mitchel recently returned from Spain, who almost immediately became involved in a legal dispute over bellanding a horse. In Milnes' time the works had two cupolas and the water-powered slagmill, and whereas Milnes had paid for damage, Mitchel was reluctant. He had introduced two new slag mills, which usually resulted in increased pollution. Reference to horizontal flues suggest these were either then introduced, or possibly extended. A further legal suit over bellanding suggests that Mitchel may have remained at Stone Edge until about 1860, after which time the works probably became disused.

In 1875 the site was sold by the Reverend Nicholas Bourne Milnes to George Mowbrey, an ancestor of the present owners of the site, the Marriott family, though he reserved the right to remove the black slag, which, from its absence, he presumably did.

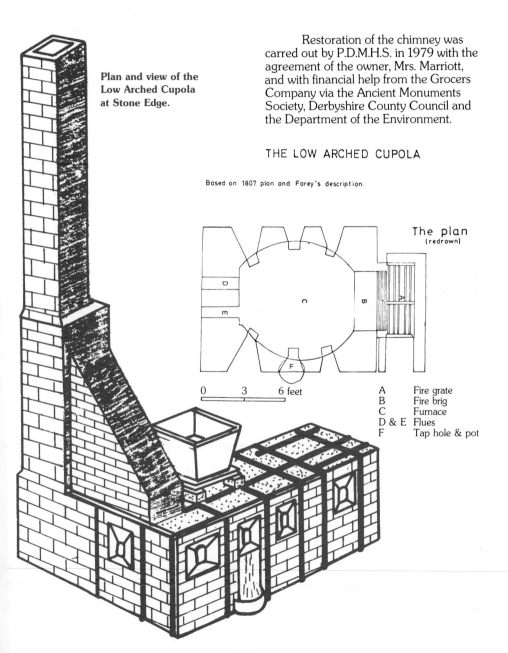

Plan and view of the Low Arched Cupola at Stone Edge.

Restoration of the chimney was carred out by P.D.M.H.S. in 1979 with the agreement of the owner, Mrs. Marriott, and with financial help from the Grocers Company via the Ancient Monuments Society, Derbyshire County Council and the Department of the Environment.

THE LOW ARCHED CUPOLA

Based on 1807 plan and Farey's description.

The plan
(redrawn)

0   3   6 feet

A	Fire grate
B	Fire brig
C	Furnace
D & E	Flues
F	Tap hole & pot

139

GOOD LUCK MINE, VIA GELLIA MIDDLETON-BY-WIRKSWORTH

2½ inches: 1 mile map SK 25; 6 inches: 1 mile map SK 25NE

The Via Gellia, the A5012, named after the Gells of Hopton, one time owners of the valley, is a typical Derbyshire dale, trending generally east-west with Cromford at its eastern end. During the early days of mining numerous mine-shafts were sunk into the veins on the hilltops overlooking the valley from both north and the south.

From the end of the 18th century attempts were made to exploit the veins at depth by driving adits into the hillside, mostly below the Matlock Lavas. A few soughs were started: even less were completed due to the lack of investment and the poor returns. Good Luck Mine is one of these adits, and is umistakeable for its prominent spoil heap is easily seen to the south of the road above the lay-by west of Marl Cottage (built from tufa got from the Dunsley Springs above).

John Alsop and Company acquired the title to Good Luck Mine by consolidating several other titles; the Goodluck founder, now lost under the 'New Turnpike Road' built in 1803 from Middleton to Ryder Point, Bals Founder (the name suggests Cornish influence), Batchelors Venture, Miners Venture and Moore Jepson Mines. This latter is now covered by Mountain Cottage, one time residence of D. H. Lawrence during the period 1919-21, when he was hounded as a pro-German sympathiser, and where he wrote "The Wintery Peacock". His mother's family (the Beardsleys) originated in the parish.

John Alsop of Lea had considerable mining interests in the area, and was typical of the entrepreneur who controlled the capitalisation of mining in the Soke and Wapentake of Wirksworth by the smelting industry. Alsop owned the smelter at Lea, together with one further down the Via Gellia in Bonsall Dale, now occupied by Cromford Garnetters and the original home of Viyella, a corruption of Via Gellia. He was to become the Barmaster for the King's Field. His partner was Joseph Hall of Lea.

Roger Knowles of Bailey's Croft, Wirksworth, agent for the owners, started work on the adit, possibly on Monday, 25th October 1830, for a record in the Barmaster's book states that on the following day, work had begun, the site having been inspected and the access route marked out as required by custom. The adit was driven into the barren limestone, for some unknown reason, on the eastern limit of the title, using hand drilling and gunpowder blasting. The spoil was taken out on 11 inches gauge tramway and tipped onto the hillside, producing the tip seen today, estimated to contain in excess of 10,000 tons of limestone.

When they had penetrated 300 feet (91 m) from the surface the miners intersected the Silver Eye Vein, then in the possession of Isaac Spencer. An agreement was made to allow Spencer access to his vein through the new adit, in return for which he agreed to pay one fifth of the cost of driving the adit to this point. This vein has now been opened up in recent years and access gained to the shaft to provide an emergency escape route.

The next vein to be intersected was one of the Black Rakes in the possession of William Greatorex and Benjamin Buckley. Another agreement was made with John Alsop and Company, but this time in return for using the adit, the miners

"Deads" supported an "herringbone" stone stemples, Hadlowfield Level, Via Gellia.
(J. H. Rieuwerts)

Good Luck Mine, Via Gellia

paid two shillings (10p) for each load of ore which had to be sold to Alsop at the current market value. This agreement did not allow for the waste stone to be removed through this adit and this had to be 'laid within the cheeks of their own veins or scrins'. Finally, after about a year's work through 'dead' limestone, the Goodluck Vein was intersected, at the top of an incline formed to raise the workings above a clay wayboard, approximately 600 feet (183 m) from the entrance. They must have been very disappointed for the vein below the lava proved to be very poor indeed.

The galena is granular, in a gangue of baryte, the vein being seldom thicker than 50mm, and 25mm is common. The proportion of galena in the baryte vein averages five percent. This meant a considerable amount of unproductive work in cutting the cheeks of the vein to give working width. The deads so produced were stacked onto stone stemples in the classical tradition of stoping. These packs together with the stempling are some of the finest to be seen in the area. The stoping was both above and below the wagon gate. The upper stopes are accessible, in places rising 60 feet above the level but the under stopes are backfilled although a shaft has been re-excavated to a depth of 60 feet (18 m) and has yet to be bottomed. By this shaft is a branch called Warl Gate, the entrance to which bears the initials of the miners and the date, 5th December 1831. Amongst others, the initials of the agent Roger Knowles are recorded.

The Goodluck Vein was fully exploited for its length within the consolidated title. Cross cuts were mined, usually following scrins in the search for further veins. Warl Gate was driven to Holmes Vein; an unnamed cross cut was driven through the old Bakers Venture title, but the principal one was Gulph Gate, driven to intersect Else Scrin, (named after a local mineral agent), Earl Grey Scrin and William IVth Scrin; these latter two were named to commemorate the passing of the Reform Act in 1832. The miners then continued to the southeastern limit of the title 'under Arthur Spencer's Barn'. They exploited Godbers Scrin, a similar vein to Goodluck Vein which Gulph Gate intersected and which runs parallel to Goodluck Vein. This was an even poorer producer, there being no attempt at under-stoping and only a little over-stoping. It would appear to have been an exploratory level.

Godber's Scrin intersects the only natural rift in the entire mine, where water is evident, and at this point the miners undertook a little underground ore-washing. A start was made in the 1840's to extend this level into Bondog Mine in the adjoining title, with a view to making the raising of ore more economical, but the scheme was abandoned. Evidence of this venture can still be seen, in the farthest reaches of the workings.

By 1840 the mine was worked out and it can only be assumed, in the absence of reckoning books, that it could not have been a profitable undertaking. It has since been worked from time to time for galena and baryte; fluorspar "sand" and copper ores in the form of azurite and a little malachite have also been found.

A little galena extraction took place in the 1950's, when the landowner blew the entrance in to prevent illegal mining. Some of the surface waste was worked for baryte in the 1920's.

On 25th May 1972, the title was given to two members of the Peak District Mines Historical Society, by the process of 'nicking', through the Great Barmote Court, 140 years after the Alsop consolidation. The mine was reopened and

Good Luck Mine, Via Gellia

is still in the possession of R. Amner, a member of the society, who opens it regularly for visitors. In this mine, one can still experience something of the life of the 'old man', for there are no concessions to flood-lighting, concrete pathways and the like. The Gulph Fault can be seen where the miners tunneled through it; there are artifacts on display where they were used, and the coes, powder house and bousesteads (ore-store) in ruins on the surface. Excavation revealed some of the lead ore still in storage!

Anyone wishing to visit the mine should contact the owner, Ron Amner, c/o The Peak District Mining Museum, The Grand Pavilion, Matlock Bath.

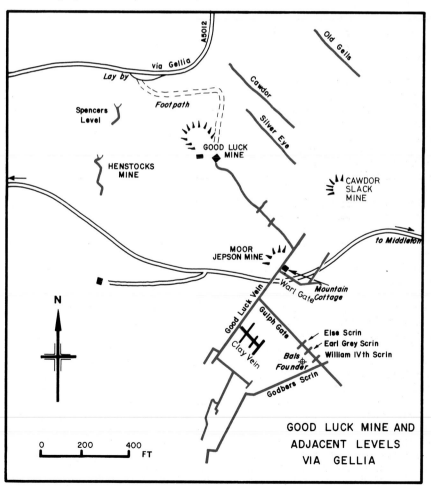

GOOD LUCK MINE AND ADJACENT LEVELS VIA GELLIA

Scrin veins seen in the roof of Good Luck Mine, Via Gellia.
(J. H. Rieuwerts)

INDEX OF MINES AND VEINS

GLOSSARY

The terms listed below are the commonest of some 600 words, which are peculiar to the Derbyshire lead mining area, or which have special meaning there. The meanings given are the usual ones, but many had different shades of meaning in different parts of the area. A full list is given in Derbyshire Lead Mining Glossary by N. Kirkham, published by the Cave Research Group of Great Britain in 1949.

Adit — a horizontal tunnel into a mine from a hillside, often called a level, and sometimes functioning as a sough.

Adventurers — shareholders in a mine or sough.

Barmaster — the representative of the Crown, responsible for the administration of mining law, measuring ore, measuring out meers along a length of vein.

Barmote (=Barmoot) — the lead miners' court, usually held twice a year in each liberty, with a jury, once 24 in number, now 12, charged with judicial duties continuously from the sitting of one court until the next. The jury is called "The Body of the Mine".

Barytes — the mineral barium sulphate ($BaSO_4$); commonly called cawk, calk, caulk or heavy spar.

Basset — the outcrop of a vein or stratum.

Belland — finely powdered lead ore. It may cause poisoning in animals and men if allowed to flow into streams or on to grass. Animals so poisoned are said to be "belland(ed)".

Bing — large pieces of ore drawn from the mine and requiring little further dressing.

Black Jack — sulphide of zinc (ZnS), properly known as sphalerite. The chief ore of zinc.

Blende — the same as black jack.

Blue John — banded blue and white fluospar, found only at Treak Cliff, Castleton.

Bole — a primitive smelting hearth, often on a hilltop, hence Bole Hill as a common place name.

Bouse — lead ore as raised from the mine before dressing.

Bucker — a broad, flat-headed hammer used mainly by women to break up ore to separate it from the gangue minerals.

Buddle — a wooden or stone trough or troughs used to wash light materials over baffles which catch the lead ore particles after crushing. To buddle is the act of so washing the ore.

Calcite — the mineral calcium carbonate ($CaCO_3$); sometimes worked as a calc-spar for decorative or building purposes.

Calk, caulk, or cawk — barytes, barium sulphate, also known as heavy spar. The chief source of barium chemicals in industry.

Calamine — zinc carbonate ($ZnCO_3$), the cream-coloured oxidation mineral resulting from the weathering of blende, often known as "dry-bone". Used in cosmetics, medicine and formerly in the manufacture of brass.

149

Cat Dirt	— decomposed toadstone, weathered basalt lava.
Channel	— decomposed toadstone.
Cheeks	— the sides or walls of a vein.
Chert	— a hard siliceous rock, like flint, found as nodules and layers in the limestone. Often black, but may weather white. It may replace limestone with enclosed fossil crinoids and is then known as 'screwstone'.
Coe	— a small shed, usually of stone, above or near a mine, in which the miners kept their tools, and sometimes a change of clothing. The climbing shaft was often under a trap door in the floor of the coe.
Cope	— a duty paid by miners to the Lord, by virtue of which they may sell their ore to whom they wish, and which may be a fixed price per load paid by the miners by agreement with the mine agent.
Corfe or Corve	— a crude wooden sledge used to convey ore, etc. underground, sometimes along wooden rails.
Cross-cut	— a passage cut through solid rock from one vein to another.
Cupola	— a reverberatory furnace for smelting lead ore.
Deads	— useless stone from a vein or working, usually stacked in abandoned workings, often on timber platforms which are now dangerously unstable.
Dial	— a miners' compass used in surveying underground.
Dish	— the measure for lead ore, either oblong or circular, varying from liberty to liberty, but generally holding between 14 and 15 Winchester pints. Nine dishes = one load; one dish = about 65 lbs.; approximately $3\frac{1}{2}$ – 4 loads = 1 ton. A standard dish made in 1512 is kept at the Moot Hall, Wirksworth.
Dolomite	— the mineral, or the rock composed dominantly of it, calcium magnesium carbonate ($CaMg(CO_3)_2$). Outcrops chiefly around Brassington and Elton. Sometimes used as a source of refractory brick material, or as a source of magnesium metal.
Dunstone	— generally applied to dolomite rock, but has been applied to toadstone, or to ironstone in different areas.
Egg and Eye	— the notch and slot made in opposite walls of a vein to hold a stemple or wooden beam.
Engine	— applied to any winding or pumping machinery, whether worked by hand, horse or steam.
Engine-shaft	— a larger shaft equipped with winding machinery rather than a stowes (windlass).
Fangs	— wood or metal pipes used to convey fresh air to the workings.
Fathom	— a measure of 6 feet, commonly used to express the depth of mines and shafts.
Fissures	— cracks or joints in the rocks, either open or filled with loose stones.
Firing	— fire-setting – the practice before the days of explosives, of lighting a fire against the face of the vein to open cracks, and make it more easy to extract the lead ore. By law it could only be done after 4 p.m.
Flat	— a body of ore generally lying more or less horizontally, of equal length and width, usually parallel with the stratification of the enclosing limestone. By elongation flats grade into pipes.
Fluorspar	— the mineral fluorite, calcium fluoride (CaF_2), widely used as a flux in blast furnaces and as a source of fluorine in chemical industry. Also used for special glasses and ceramics.
Forefield	— the working face of a mine, usually the furthest point from the shaft.

Fother	— a measure of lead, normally by volume, occasionally in recent times by weight, in both cases varying from liberty to liberty, ranging from 1,680 lbs. to 2,520 lbs. usually nearer the latter.
Founder	— the first miner to work a mine; or the first meers allocated by the barmaster to found the mine; or the first shaft sunk.
Freeing	— the act of delivering to the barmaster a dish of ore to establish ownership of a new vein or mine.
Galena	— the mineral lead sulphide (PbS). The chief ore of lead.
Gang, or Gangue	— the waste minerals found with the lead ore, usually dumped on the hillock. Since the minerals include fluorspar and barytes, they are now often more valuable than the lead and many hillocks have been reprocessed for the gangue.
Gate	— a way or passage in a mine; an access route.
Gin	— a winding engine; a horse-gin, driven by horses; also known as a whim.
Gin circle	— the circular area, round which the horse plodded to work the gin.
Ginging	— the dressed stonework around the top parts of a shaft holding up the loose ground.
Grove or Groove	— a mine; sometimes applied to a length of vein being worked more or less as a single mine; sometimes restricted to open workings at the surface.
Hade	— the slope of a vein from the vertical.
Heading	— alternative name for a cross-cut, gate or adit.
Hillocks, hillocking	— old tip heaps, searching them for unrecovered minerals.
Icles, water-icicles, watricle	— stalactites, as found in caves.
Jagger	— one who carried lead ore from the mines to the smelting place on pack-horses.
Jig	— a concentrating device used to separate the lead ore from the gangue.
Kebble. Kibble	— a large bucket used to lift the ore up the shaft.
Level	— a horizontal tunnel, adit, sough or gate. A level may also be a surveying instrument.
Liberty	— the district in which the miner searches for ore. Derbyshire has several liberties with slightly differing laws and customs.
Load	— a measure of lead ore, being 9 dishes, varying between 3½ and 4 loads to a ton.
Lord	— the owner of the mineral liberty, who receives the "lot", and usually also the "cope".
Lord's Meer	— a length of vein laid out by the barmaster for the lord, who receives all the ore obtained from it, or makes special arrangements with the miners.
Lot	— the share of ore to the lord, usually every 13th dish, though he may take anything from the 10th to the 25th according to the Liberty and other circumstances, measured at reckonings every 6 weeks or so.
Marble	— in the geological sense it is strictly a limestone which has been recrystallized by the subsequent applications of heat and pressure. Commercially the term "marble" is applied to any limestone which will take a polish.

Meer	— a measure of length of a vein, varying in different liberties, 27, 28, 29, 30 or 32 yards. Two founder meers are usually allocated to the discoverers of a vein. Taker meers are added later. Lord's Meer is the one allocated to the lord, usually next to the founder meers.
Mine Royal	— a mine containing gold or silver to a value greater than that of the associated base metals.
Nicking	— failure to work a mine may allow another miner to claim it, by asking the barmaster to "nick", i.e. cut a piece out of, the stowes. Three nickings allow the mine to be forfeited and handed over to the claimant, unless excess water or lack of ventilation prevent the mine being worked.
Offal	— waste, gangue and rock, sometimes including unrecoverable lead ore.
Old Man	— (t'owd man) places worked by former miners; or the former miners themselves.
Open	— a naturally open cavern or fissure.
Ore	— the valuable mineral from which a metal can be extracted. In Derbyshire it refers only to lead ore, galena.
Pig	— the block of cast lead metal in the smelter's works. Commonly 8 pigs make one fother.
Pipe	— a body of ore lying more or less horizontally, but long and narrow. Grades into a flat by broadening. Many pipe-veins are in fact ancient caverns filled with ore and gangue. Pipes may branch out of rakes.
Quarter Cord	— ground allowed to the miner either side of a vein to deposit his refuse and build his coe, a quarter of a meer in width.
Rake	— the main type of mineral vein in the Peak District. A body of ore and gangue minerals disposed vertically between two walls of rock, and thus having a straight course across country. Rakes may be up to several miles long, but grade in size down into scrins, which are, broadly speaking, small rakes.
Rider	— a mass of rock dividing a vein. Also known as a horse.
Rise	— an underground shaft driven upwards above a working.
Scrin	— a short, often thin, vertical vein of ore; often branching out of a rake.
Self-open	— a large natural cavern.
Shack	— a natural opening in the ground; also known as a shake, or shake-hole, sometimes filled with loose rocks.
Shale-gate	— a tunnel cut through shale.
Sinkers	— the men who make shafts.
Slag	— the waste material produced during smelting lead ore.
Slickensides	— the shiny, grooved surfaces produced by movements of the strata along geological faults. Sometimes still in a state of stress, and liable to explode on being disturbed by mining.
Smelting	— extracting the lead metal from the ore.
Smitham	— finely powdered ore produced by the crusher.
Sole	— the floor of a mine or sough; the lowest level worked.
Sough	— an adit or tunnel driven specifically to drain a mine.
Soughers	— those who dig soughs.
Spar	— a collective term for the crystalline minerals found with lead-ore; variously applied to fluorspar, barytes (heavy spar), calcite, (calc-spar).

Stemple	— a piece of wood wedged across a working or vein, for use as a rung of a climbing way, or as part of a platform or lodgement for stacking deads, or part of a roof support. Stemples of dressed stone occur in a few mines.
Steward	— the presiding officer of the Barmote Court. The lord's executive.
Stope	— a worked-out vein left as an open cavity.
Stowes **(stoes, stoce)**	— the wooden windlass over a shaft for raising ore. The stowes had to be made to a definite pattern, and the existence of a pair of stowes (i.e. one windlass) was a symbol of ownership of a mine.
Strike	— the course or direction of a vein or stratum.
Sump	— any vertical opening in a mine not connecting to the surface; an internal shaft; sometimes called a winze or turn. Alternatively a sump is a hollow in the bottom of a mine for collecting the drainage before pumping.
Swallow **or Swallet**	— a natural opening which takes water away.
Tailings	— the finely ground waste from a modern ore-processing plant.
Toadstone	— a collective name for several types of basaltic volcanic rock. It may be compact basalt, or may have vesicles (gas-bubble cavities), or may be decomposed to a green clay, or may be rubbly volcanic ash.
Turn	— an underground shaft, also called a sump or a winze.
Turntree	— alternative term for a stowes.
The Twenty-four	— the Grand Jury of the Barmote Court, the "Body of the Mine".
Vein	— the body of minerals enclosed by rock.
Vein-stuff	— the minerals, etc. in a vein.
Wad	— impure manganese ore, a mixture of iron and manganese oxides.
Water-gate	— a sough or drainage level.
Water-icicles **watricles**	— stalactites.
Way-board	— a clay bed between beds of limestone, usually not more than a few inches thick.
Wheat-ore **White ore**	— lead carbonate, the mineral cerussite ($PbCO_3$). Worked as an ore, often used in lead paints.
Whim	— a winding engine worked by horses or steam.
Whimsey	— a steam-driven winding engine.
Winze	— a small underground shaft sunk from one part of a mine to another.
Woughs	— the limestone walls of a vein.

ACKNOWLEDGMENTS

This book could not have been compiled without the co-operation of many people in whose care there are collections of manuscripts concerned with lead-mining. In particular the authors would like to express their gratitude to the following.

The Trustees of the Chatsworth Settlement for access to the Devonshire Collections at Chatsworth House.

The Director of the Manuscript Collection in the British Museum Library for help with the Woolley Manuscripts.

The Librarian of the Local History Department, Sheffield City Libraries, for access to the Bagshawe Collection, Oakes Deeds and Wager Holmes collection.

The Derbyshire County Library for access to manuscripts.
Miss J. Sinar of the Derbyshire Record Office for access to the Brooke-Taylor documents and many others.

The late Mr. John Mort, Barmaster, and his successor Mr. W. M. Erskine, for access to the Barmaster's Books.

Mr. B. Miller of Bagshawe, Miller & Co., Solicitors, Sheffield, for the gift of the Bagshawe-Manton documents from their office to J. Rieuwerts.

Mr. and Mrs. Marriott, the late Mr. M. Brooke-Taylor and the late Mr. R.W.P. Cockerton, for access to private documents.

The editors and authors would like to acknowledge their indebtedness to the late Miss Nellie Kirkham for her help and encouragement of all interested in the old lead mines. Without her pioneer works in this field it is doubtful if this book could have been written. The Whitworth Art Gallery, Manchester, have kindly allowed us to use a photograph of John Webber's painting of Odin Mine. Other photographs have been kindly supplied by the Derbyshire Pennine Club, Laporte Industries Ltd., Glebe Mines, Eyam, and by Messrs H. M. Parker and F. Nixon. The Midland Institute of Mining Engineers have kindly allowed us to reproduce some of A. H. Stokes' drawings from their Transactions of 1880. Others whose help has been invaluable include J. Beck, N. J. D. Butcher, R. Flindall, A. Greenwood, L. Gregory, D. Manton, Dr. W. A. S. Sarjeant.

FURTHER READING
(a) General Works

AGRICOLA, G., 1556. "De Re Metallica". (English translation by H. & L. Hoover, 1912). Dover Press.

CARRUTHERS, R. G. & STRAHAN, A. 1923. "Lead and Zinc Ores of Durham, Yorkshire and Derbyshire with notes on the Isle of Man". Geol. Surv. Spec. Rep. Min. Res. Vol. 26, pp. 41-88.

DONALD, M. B. 1961. "Elizabethan Monopolies".

DUNHAM, K. C. 1952. "Fluorspar". Geol. Surv. Spec. Rep. Min. Res., Vol. 4, 4th edition, 143p.

FAREY, J. 1811. "A General View of the Agriculture and Minerals of Derbyshire". Vol. 1. 532p.

FORD, T. D., 1969. "The Stratiform Ore Deposits of Derbyshire". pp. 73-96. in Proc. 15th Inter-University Geological Congress, Leicester, edited by C. H. James.

FORD, T.D., 1967. "Some Mineral Deposits of the Carboniferous Limestone of Derbyshire", pp. 53-75, in "Geological Excursions in the Sheffield Area and the Peak District National Park", edited by R. Neves & C. Downie, University of Sheffield.

FORD, T. D., 1976. "The ores of the South Pennines and Mendip Hills – a comparative study". in K. H. Wolf's "Handbook of stratabound and stratiform ore deposits", vol. 5, pp. 161-195. Elsevier Scientific Pub. Co.

FORD, T. D., 1977. "Limestones and Caves of the Peak District". Geo-Books, Geo-Abstracts Ltd., Norwich, 469pp.

FORD, T. D. & GILL, D. W. 1980. "Caves of Derbyshire". 4th edn. Dalesman Publ. Co., Clapham, nr Lancaster. 168pp.

FORD, T. D. & INESON, P.R. 1971. "The Fluorspar mining potential of the Derbyshire Orefield". Trans. Inst. Mining & Metallurgy. Vol. B80, pp. 186-210.

FORD, T. D. & MASON, M. H. 1967. "Bibliography of the Geology of the Peak District of Derbyshire up to 1965". Mercian Geol. Vol. 2, No. 2, pp. 133-244. Supplement in Vol. 4, No. 2, 1972.

FORD, T. D. & SARJEANT, W. A. S. 1964. "The Peak District Mineral Index". Bull. Peak Dist. Mines Hist. Soc., Vol. 2, pp. 122-150.

FULLER, J. M. 1965. "Lead Mining in Derbyshire in the mid-nineteenth Century". East Midland Geog., Vol. 3, No. 7, pp. 373-393.

GLOVER, S. 1829. "History and Gazetteer of the County of Derby". 2 Vols.

HARDY, W. 1714. "The Miners' Guide".

HARRIS. H. 1971. "Industrial Archaeology of the Peak District". David & Charles, Newton Abbot.

HOLMES, J. F. 1962. "Lead Mining in Derbyshire". Mining Mag., Vol. 107, pp. 137-148.

HOPKINSON. G. G. 1958. "Five Generations of Derbyshire Lead Mining and Smelting". Derbys. Arch. Jour., Vol. 78, pp. 9-24.

KIRKHAM, N. 1950. "Old Drowned Work in Derbyshire". Derbys. Arch. Jour., Vol. 70, pp. 1-20.

KIRKHAM, N. 1953. "The Tumultuous Course of Dovegang". Derbys. Arch. Jour., Vol. 73, pp. 1-35.

KIRKHAM, N. 1960-61. "The Draining of the Alport Mines". Trans-Newcomen. Soc., Vol. 33, pp. 67-91.

KIRKHAM, N. 1961. "Winster Sough". Bull. Peak Dist. Mines Hist. Soc., Vol. 1, No. 5, pp. 10-29

KIRKHAM, N. 1964-6. "Eyam Edge Mines and Soughs". Bull. Peak Dist. Mines Hist. Soc., Vol. 2, pp. 241-254 and 315-334; Vol. 3, pp. 43-57 and 130-118.

KIRKHAM, N. 1965-66. "Steam Engines in Derbyshire's Lead Mines". Trans. Newcomen Soc., Vol. 38.

KIRKHAM, N. 1968. "Derbyshire Lead Mining through the Centuries". Bradford Barton, Truro.

MANLOVE, E. 1653. "The Liberties and Customs of the Lead Mines within the Wapentake of Wirksworth in the County of Derby". Composed in Meter. (Reprinted in A. H. Stokes, 1880).

NIXON, F. 1957-9. "The Early Steam Engine in Derbyshire". Trans. Newcomen Soc., Vol. 31, 28p.

NIXON, F. 1969. "The Industrial Archaeology of Derbyshire". David and Charles, Newton Abbot.

O'NEAL, R. 1961. "A Bibliography of Derbyshire Lead Mining". Derbyshire County Library.

PERCY, J. 1870. "The Metallurgy of Lead". Murray, London.

RAISTRICK, A. & JENNINGS, B. 1965. "A History of Lead Mining in the Pennines". Longmans, London.

RIEUWERTS, J. H. 1963. "Lathkilldale: Its Mines and Miners". Bull. Peak Dist. Mines Hist. Soc., Vol. 2, No. 1, pp. 9-30.

RIEUWERTS, J. H. 1966. "A List of the Soughs of the Derbyshire Lead Mines". Bull. Peak Dist. Mines Hist. Soc., Vol. 3, No. 1, pp. 1-42. (Supplementary list in Vol. 4, No. 2), 1969.

RIEUWERTS, J. H. 1972. "Derbyshire's Old Lead Mines and Miners". Moorlands Publ. Co., Hartington.

RIEUWERTS, J. H. 1978. "The Inquisition or Quo Warrento of 1288." Bull. Peak. Dist. Mines Hist. Soc. Vol. 7, No. 1, pp. 41-49. & No. 2, pp. 96-98.

RIEUWERTS, J. H. 1980. "Derbyshire's Early Soughs" Bull. Peak Dist. Mines Hist. Soc. Vol. 7, No. 5, pp. 241-314.

RIEUWERTS, J. H. 1981. "The development of mining and drainage in the Wensley Winster and Elton areas". Bull. Peak Dist. Mines Hist. Soc. Vol. 8, No. 2, pp. 109-150.

ROBEY, J. A. & PORTER, L. 1972. "The Copper and Lead Mines of Ecton Hill, Staffordshire". Moorland Publ. Co. Ashbourne.

SMITH, E. G. RHYS, G. H. & EDEN, R. A. 1967. "Geology of the Country Around Chesterfield, Matlock and Mansfield". Mem. Geol. Surv., 430p.

STOKES, A. H. 1880-1882. "Lead and Lead-mining in Derbyshire". Trans. Chesterfield & Derbys. Inst. Min. Civ. Mech. Eng. (reprinted 1973 as Peak Dist. Mines Hist. Soc. Spec. Pub. No. 2).

STEVENSON, I. P. & GAUNT, G. D. 1971. "Geology of the Country Around Chapel-en-le-Frith (and Castleton)". Inst. Geol. Sciences, London (H.M.S.O.).

SYLVESTER-BRADLEY, P.C. & FORD, T.D.. 1968. "Geology of the East Midlands". Univ. Leicester Press, 400p.

TAYLOR, L. F. 1958. "Mill Close Mine". Derbyshire Countryside.

VARVILL, W. W. 1959. "The Future of Lead-Zinc and Fluorspar Mining in Derbyshire". In Symposium on the Future of Non-ferrous Mining in Great Britain. Inst. Min. Met., pp. 175-232.

VARVILL, W. W. 1962. "Secondary Enrichment by Natural Flotation". Mine and Quarry Eng. Vol. 27. pp. 64-73, 112-118, 156-161, 208-214.

WILLIES, L. 1971. "The Introduction of the Cupola to Derbyshire". Bull. Peak Dist. Mines Hist. Soc., Vol. 4, pp. 384-394.

WILLIES, L. 1969. "Cupola Lead Smelting Sites in Derbyshire, 1737-1900." Bull. Peak Dist. Mines Hist. Soc., Vol. 4, pp. 97-115.

WILLIES, L. M. 1979. "Technical development in Derbyshire lead mining 1700-1880". Bull. Peak Dist. Mines Hist. Soc. Vol. 7, No. 3, pp. 117-151.

WILLIES, L. M., RIEUWERTS, J. H. & FLINDALL, R. 1977. "Wind, water and steam engines of Derbyshire lead mines: a list. Bull. Peak Dist. Mines Hist. Soc. Vol. 6, No. 6, pp. 303-320.

(b) References for the itineraries

1. Castleton

FORD, T. D. 1980. "Treak Cliff Cavern and Blue John stone". Guide book, Treak Cliff Cavern, Castleton.

FORD, T. D. 1955. "Blue John Fluorspar". Proc. Yorks. Geol. Soc. Vol. 30, pp. 35-60.

FORD, T. D. 1982. "The Speedwell Mine, Castleton", Guide book, the Speedwell Mine.

FORD, T. D. & RIEUWERTS, J. H. 1976. "Odin Mine, Castleton", Bull. Peak Dist. Mines Hist. Soc. Vol. 6, No. 4, pp. 1-54.

2. Eyam and Stoney Middleton

ANON. 1965. "The Cavendish Mill (and Glebe Mines)". Minerals & Mining Eng., Vol. 1, No. 15, pp. 579-586.

ANON. 1968. "Mining at Sallet Hole". Minerals and Mining Eng, Vol. 4, No. 3, pp. 105-106.

ANON. 1965. "Fluorspar Flotation at Glebe Mines". Mining Mag., Vol. 113, pp. 276-283.

KIRKHAM, N. 1964-6. "Eyam Edge Mines and Soughs". Bull. Peak Dist. Mines Hist. Soc. Vol. 2, pp. 241-254, 315, 335; Vol. 3, pp. 43-57, 103-118.

KIRKHAM, N. 1966. "Longstone Edge Mines and Soughs". Part 1. Cave Science. Vol. 5, No. 39, pp. 354-368; Part 2, Cave Science, Vol. 6, No. 40, pp. 440-469.

WILLIES, L. 1974. "The Lords Cupola, Stoney Middleton". Bull. Peak Dist. Mines Hist. Soc. Vol. 5, pp. 288-301.

3. Magpie Mine & Sheldon

ROBEY, J. A. 1966. "Fieldgrove Mine". Bull. Peak Dist. Mines Hist. Soc. Vol. 3, pp. 93-101.

WILLIES, L. 1974. "The Re-opening of the Magpie Sough". Bull. Peak Dist. Mines Hist. Soc. Vol. 5, pp. 324-331.

WILLIES, L. M., ROCHE, V.S., WORLEY, N. E. & FORD, T.D. 1980. "The History of Magpie Mine, Sheldon, Derbyshire". Peak Dist. Mines Hist. Soc. Spec. Publn. No. 3, 4th edn. 56pp.

4. Ashford Black Marble Mines

FORD, T. D. 1958. "The Black Marble of Ashford-in-the-Water". Liverpool & Manchester Geol. Jour., Vol. 2, pp. 44-59.

FORD, T. D. 1964. "The Black Marble Mines of Ashford-in-the-Water". Bull. Peak Dist. Mines Hist. Soc. Vol. 2, No. 4, pp. 179-188.

5. Lathkilldale

RIEUWERTS, J.H. 1963. "Lathkill Dale: Its Mines and Miners". Bull. Peak Dist. Mines Hist. Soc. Vol. 2, pp. 9-30.

RIEUWERTS, J.H. 1973. "Lathkill Dale: Its Mines and Miners". Moorland Publ. Co., Hartington.

TUNE, R. 1969. "A Survey of Mandale Mine". Bull. Peak Dist. Mines Hist. Soc., Vol. 4, No. 1, pp. 67-74.

6. Monyash Mines

KITCHEN, G. & PENNEY, D. 1973. "New Pumps for Old", Bull. Peak Dist. Mines Hist. Soc., Vol. 5, pp. 129-136.

ROBEY, J. A. 1961-63. "The Mines North-west of Monyash, Parts 1-3". Bull. Peak Dist. Mines Hist. Soc. Vol. 1, No. 5, pp. 30-36; Vol. 1, No. 6, pp. 29-32; Vol. 2, No. 1, pp. 51-56.

ROBEY, J. A. 1965. "The Drainage of the Area Between the Rivers Wye and Lathkill". Proc. Brit. Speleo. Assoc., No. 3, pp. 1-10.

ROBEY, J. A. 1973. "Supplementary Notes on the Monyash-Flagg Area". Bull. Peak Dist. Mines Hist. Soc. Vol. 5, pp. 149-155.

7. Alport

KIRKHAM, N. 1960-61. "The Drainage of the Alport Mines". Trans. Newcomen Soc., Vol. 33, pp. 67-91.

KIRKHAM, N. 1965-66. "Steam Engines in Derbyshire's Lead Mines". Trans. Newcomen Soc., Vol. 38, pp. 69-88.

KIRKHAM, N. 1964-65. "The Ventilation of Hillcarr Sough". Trans. Newcomen Soc., Vol. 37, pp. 133-138.

RIEUWERTS, J. H. 1981. "The drainage of the Alport Mining Field". Bull. Peak Dist. Mines Hist. Soc. Vol. 8, No. 1, pp. 1-28.

8. Matlock and Cromford

BRYAN, B. 1903. "Matlock Manor and Parish".

FLINDALL, R. & HAYES, A. 1972. "Wapping Mine and Cumberland Cavern, Matlock Bath". Bull. Peak Dist. Mines Hist. Soc., Vol. 5, pp.114-127.

FLINDALL, R. & HAYES, A. 1973. "The Mines near Upperwood – the Tear Breeches-Hopping-Fluorspar-Speedwell complex". Bull. Peak Dist. Mines Hist. Soc., Vol. 5, pp. 182-199.

FLINDALL, R. & HAYES, A. 1976. "The Caverns and Mines of Matlock Bath: 1 the Nestus Mines: Rutland and Masson Caverns". Moorland, Ashbourne. 72 pp.

HURT, L. 1970. "A Survey of Ball Eye Mines, Bonsall". Bull. Peak Dist. Mines Hist. Soc., Vol. 4, pp. 289-305.

KIRKHAM, N. 1963. "Old Mill Close Lead Mine". Bull. Peak Dist. Mines Hist. Soc., Vol. 2, No. 1, pp. 70-82.

KIRKHAM, N. 1963. "The Draining of Wirksworth Lead Mines". Derbyshire Arch. Soc. Local Hist. Sect., 19 pp.

RAISTRICK, A. 1937. "Mill Close Mine in Derbyshire". Proc. Univ. Durham Phil. Soc., Vol. 10, pp. 38-47.

TRAILL, J. G. 1939. "The Geology and Development of Mill Close Mine". Econ. Geol., Vol. 34, pp. 851-889.

WARRINER, D., WILLIES, L. M. & FLINDALL, R. 1981. "Ringing Rake and Masson Soughs and the mines on the east side of Masson Hill, Matlock". Bull. Peak Dist. Mines Hist. Soc., Vol. 8, No. 2, pp. 109-150.

VARVILL, W. W. 1937. "A Study of the Shapes and Distribution of Lead Deposits in the Pennines". Trans. Inst. Min. Met., Vol. 46, pp. 463-559.

VARVILL, W. W. 1962. "Secondary Enrichment by Natural Flotation". Mine & Quarry Eng., Vol. 27, pp. 64-73, 112-118, 156-161, 208-214.

9. Crich

BEMROSE, H. H. ARNOLD. 1894. "Notes on Crich Hill". Derbys. Arch. Jour., Vol. 16, pp. 44-51.

GREGORY, N. 1966. "Notes and Impressions of Jingler Mine, Wakebridge". Bull. Peak Dist. Mines Hist. Soc., Vol. 3, pp. 58-62.

KIRKHAM, N. 1957. "Ridgeway Level, Whatstandwell". Derbyshire Miscellany, Vol. 1, No. 6, pp. 72-75.

KIRKHAM, N. 1969. "Lead Mining at Crich". Manchester Assoc. of Eng. Proc. 133th session, No. 5, 17 pp.

10. Carsington Pastures

FORD, T. D. & KING, R. J. 1965. "Layered Epigenetic Galena-barite Deposits in the Golconda Mine, Brassington". Econ. Geol., Vol. 60, pp. 1686-1701.

FORD, T. D. & KING, R. J. 1966. "The Golconda Caverns". Trans. Cave Research Group G. B., Vol. 7, No. 2, pp. 91-114.

11. Stone Edge Cupola

WILLIAMS, C. J. & WILLIES, L. 1968. "Stone Edge Cupola". Bull. Peak Dist. Mines Hist. Soc., Vol. 3 pp. 315-322.

WILLIES, L. 1969. "Cupola Lead-smelting Sites in Derbyshire. 1737-1900". Bull. Peak Dist. Mines Hist. Soc., Vol. 4, No. 1, pp. 97-115.

WILLIES, L. 1972. "Gabriel Jars (1732-1769) and the Derbyshire Lead Industry". Bull. Peak Dist. Mines Hist. Soc., Vol. 5, pp. 31-39.

12. Good Luck Mine, Via Gellia

WILLIES, L. 1969, "Cupola Lead Smelting Sites in Derbyshire 1737-1900". Bulletin P.D.M.H.S. Vol. 4, part 1, pp. 97-115.

FLINDALL, R. & HAYES, A. 1972, "A Survey of Goodluck Mine and Adjacent Levels in the Via Gellia". Bull P.D.M.H.S., Vol. 5, part 1, pp. 61-80.

AMNER, R. & NAYLOR, P. 1973, "Goodluck Mine, Via Gellia". Bull. P.D.M.H.S., Vol. 5, part 4, pp. 217-240.

THE BULLETIN OF THE PEAK DISTRICT MINES HISTORICAL SOCIETY

THE BULLETIN, first published in 1959, is issued twice yearly without charge to paid-up members of the Society – non-members wishing to buy copies should contact the Secretary at the address below.

Volume 1 was published in 7 parts (1959-1962); all subsequent volumes are in 6 parts: volume 7 was completed in 1980. Many parts are still available from M. Luff, c/o The Mining Museum, Matlock Bath.

Enquiries concerning membership and subscriptions should be sent to the Secretary, P.D.M.H.S., The Mining Museum, The Pavilion, Matlock Bath, Derbyshire.

From time to time the Society publishes SPECIAL PUBLICATIONS which are charged separately to members and non-members alike, for example: "The History of Magpie Mine, Sheldon" by L. M. Willies and others, 4th Edn., 1980 – obtainable from the Mining Museum.